B.J. McKendry.

Enjoy the read.

Life Happens

by Janette McKendry

Previous books by the author

Ballyclare Remembered
More Tales to Tell
Snippets of Life

Published in 2016 by Shanway Press,
15 Crumlin Road, Belfast BT14 6AA

Cover design: David-Lee Badger

ISBN: 978-1-910044-11-7

For this my fourth book, I once again have to thank Lindy for her nimble fingers putting my scribbling (and bad spelling) into some kind of order and the staff at Shanway for their help as always with the layout.

As with the earlier books this one is based on our ordinary lives. People tell me their stories. Some say please don't use my name and of course their wishes are respected, but this in no way detracts from the tales. Some stories are told in rhyme which I hope everyone will enjoy. While it may not be the world's best poetry it is simply meant to tell the story in the way that, to me, seemed best at the time.

Some stories may make you smile, some make you almost weep, but we meet laughter and tears every day. I hope you enjoy these short journeys through other folks' lives.

Index

This year being the hundredth anniversary of the First World War, known now as The Great War, it seemed only right to include a mention of the ordinary men who went to fight for freedom.

The Hospital Tent

Inside the makeshift ward the wounded lay.
Think nought that these were hardened men
Tutored in ways of war.
Their government had called them
From factory, farm and fen
It put a rifle in their hand
To kill their fellow men.

Sam Todd was a baker from London town
And Sean farmed a green Antrim hill.
There was Rab from Dundee,
And Taffy from Wales
And eighteen year old John
From an orchard near Rhyll.

One suffered chest wounds, one had no sight.
Two each lost a leg, still they hobbled along.
Young John, his wounds were
Most serious of all.
Shattered limbs and memory gone,
His dark hours filled with pain
Til' an hour before the dawn.

The doctor came. He looked and walked away,
Despairing at the horror of it all.
Outside the stench of war
Lay heavy under sodden sky,
Where ne'er was heard the skylarks call.
Only mortar blasts were heard, while
Cloying mud claimed floor and canvas wall.

John's voice rang out, "Ma, the orchard's in bloom
The sky is blue and the air is clean".
Unseen, death walked the ward
Halting at the youngster's bed.
Death, kindly now reached down to claim
And cradle close the lad
While wrapped in his sunlit dream.

A Politician's Nightmare

Amanda bustled into the room, all of a flutter. She could hardly wait to get sat down to her cup of tea and two cream buns, before the words started burbling out of her mouth, spewing crumbs and cream all over her knees and on to the floor around her chair.

"You'll never guess who I saw down the street, with the rest of that crowd. Them ones promising us all sorts of things they have no intention of doing. It was your man and there he was as proud as a peacock. Man did he think he was no goat's toe, spouting out a lot of guff, like he knew what he was talking about."

Nora looked puzzled, "Amanda, I don't know who you're talking about. What's his name?"

"Ugh, I forget, but he went to school with us. Way back then he was a bit of a know-all. Sure his mammy was always telling him how special he was, an' how he was a cut above the rest of us. Do ye not mind the wee fella in the second row, with his hair plastered to his crown? All he needed was hair on his top lip an' he'd have looked like Hitler."

Shaking her head, Nora said, "I still can't place him."

"Nora, you do remember him", Amanda told her. "You'll remember this. When the rest of the boys were put into long trousers, he was still wearin' knee socks, with his trousers half way up his thighs. Do you not remember the rest of the boys keepin' him goin' about it? Surely you can't have forgotten the day it was so cold he wet his trousers, before he could run across the playground to the toilets"

"Ah, sure I remember that, the poor wee fella. Mind you we all laughed at the time. Isn't it strange the things we remember folk for. Gosh I don't think I could take him seriously when I think about that."

Amanda shook her head, "Same with me. I'll tell you one thing. I'll bet he's hoping none of us remembers that now."

Nora stood up to clear the cups away. "Well", she said. "One thing is certain. The past will catch you up when you least want or expect it to."

The Haircut

Sometimes Boyd Millar, he of the push-bike tale in my
first book, cut the odd head of hair. Not, of course, in a
shop or hairdressing establishment. Oh no. That would
have been too run of the mill to fit in with his free as air
kind of life. Boyd's haircuts were given in the open air.
Anywhere - field, garden or lane, wherever was
convenient at the time. The following rhyme shows how
the odd disloyal customer could be treated.

Boyd's Haircut

"Hi you" said Boyd as he walked by with his bike,
"Whoever done that tae yer hair?
Thy gien nae thought tae what suits yea
But maybe yea dinnae much care.
If yea did yea wouldnae pass by me,
For that galoot down the street.
Hairdresser be dammed, sure hes heid's shaved,
An' he's tattooed fie his brow tae his feet.

Go in an' tak a luk at yersel'
Ye'd pass fer a rat wae nae grace.
A heid like yours needs a careful cut,
Tae tak the bad luk aff yer face.
Now me, ad hae done a lot better,
An' I'd cost yea a few bob less.
I'd a made yea a dream o' a fella.
Instead yer a total disgrace"
Boyd was a one off. New comers to the town were
surprised at the respect he was given by those who grew
up in the area and who knew him when Ballyclare was
still a large village. When genuine eccentrics like him
disappear a little bit of colour fades from the life of the
town.

The House on the Corner

The little house sits on the end of a row of small terraced houses. On its gable end is a sign directing worshippers to the Covenanters Church round the corner. Once these houses had been finished in red brick but now they are various shades of tans and creams and some are pebble-dashed.

The house at the end and on the corner where the Ballyeaston Road is joined by the Ballycorr Road was once painted a dull shade of grey and was passed many times each day by those carrying buckets of water from the cow-tail pump , which sat a few yards down the Ballycorr Road.

Once this house had been Liza Jane Boyd's grocery shop with its windows opening on to both roads and the door opening out, before anyone passing reached the pump. New comers to the town have no idea of the stories this little house could tell if it could but speak.

I have already related, in one of my earlier books, how, many years ago the children used to tie their skipping ropes round the lamp post at the corner. They would swing round and round, giggling and laughing, until the day when a little girl got tangled up in her rope and was strangled – children no longer swung round the lamp post.

The fifties saw clear summer nights when the young fellows would gather at this spot. Sitting on the cribbin, they would sing folk songs and popular melodies, while people stood listening in their doorways, sat on the

window sills or danced waltzes and barn dances, on the junction, where the two roads meet, until the coming night swallowed the daylight.

Patsy and Bobby McCudden took over the shop, Liza Jane having moved to larger premises down the road to beside Alex and Evelyn Agnew's sweet shop. Patsy and Bobby modernised the little shop and ran a successful business for many years. When they retired and moved on, a family with children moved in and lived happily there for quite a few years.

One dreadful night a fire broke out in the corner house. Consternation and horror filled the minds of those living close by. The blaze was fierce. Neighbours helped where they could before the fire brigade arrived. Soon hoses were trained on the inferno. Ladders reached the upstairs window, above the back yard. One by one the rescuers helped the family, coughing and breathing with difficulty, to safety. Soon all were out – all save the mother, who when she appeared at the window, hesitated and despite much encouragement could not be persuaded to step onto the ladder. Instead, before disbelieving eyes, she turned back into the smoke and flames.

The question why can be asked over and over again, but still no answer will come. Was it some sort of fear of stepping on to the ladder, or a horror of being seen in night clothes or was it some precious memento she hoped to save? No one will ever know. Her sorrowing family were left to grieve for a much loved wife and mother with the unanswerable question. Why?

The bricks and mortar hold fast their secrets.

Rules! What Rules?

Any town or village that has at least one eccentric is indeed fortunate. These individuals live by no-one's rules but their own. They do things just because they want to and refuse to be bound by the rules that most of us place on ourselves and other people. Usually when speaking about them we say "Wee so and so did ..." and the tale follows.

Wee Tam Mahaffy, in the 50s ran a very successful bicycle shop on Main Street. It was a two storey building attached to one end of Caddy,s Row, a row of white washed stone cottages running from the back end of Tam,s shop, along the Mill Lane at their back, with the fields opening on to the dirt lane down their front, which faced the long brick side of 'The Reo', the local picture house. At the other end of the row was a small room used by the local flute band. Before this it had been a dance hall going by the glorious name of 'The Greasy Pig'.

He was never known just as Wee Tam as this would have indicated acceptance, or even liking, and this was not the case. Wee Tam Mahaffy, always he got his full title, stood about four foot seven inches tall with his boots on. Black haired and with that pale, deeply lined skin and greyish pallor that always looks ill or unwashed, his face seemed always to be set in a permanent scowl.

His business prospered, not because of his charm but because in his establishment, a bike could be purchased for ten shillings down and half a crown each week until it was paid off. This suited most people, especially the young fellas, who in those far off days never even dreamt of owning a car.

On entering his shop usually no one could be seen. The unwary might be tempted to make an uncomplimentary comment about the state of the place or on the owner himself. Suddenly Tam's head would appear above the high counter, he having stepped up onto the box, kept behind there to raise him to the necessary height to enable him to conduct business. Out from behind the counter he would race, face set in determined anger, and grab the speaker by the back of his collar and the seat of his pants and deposit him unceremoniously on the cribben outside, much to the amusement of passers-by, who knew exactly what had been the cause of the fearsome sudden exit.

Another eccentric was Scobae, who unlike Tam was looked on with great affection by the folk of the town, though he was never called wee. "Have you seen what Scobae's up to now?" someone would ask and we would wait for the latest antic to be related. For a long time it was his habit to walk round with his jacket off his shoulders, hanging almost to his elbows. He looked quite nonchalant as he strolled along, cap set on his head in a jaunty angle. When he tired of this he could be seen walking around with what looked like a slender tree trunk across his shoulders, arms curled round the branch and cap tilted on his head. There was of course no reason for this. It was just what he wanted to do at that moment in time.

When he tired of this he would lay out a picnic on one of the seats in the Square, not that he wanted anything to eat, he simply enjoyed sitting there nodding to all in general. After a time he tired of the picnic and moved on to a more upmarket tableau. He would lay a cloth on a seat at the roundabout at the top of the town and on it he would place a couple of wine glasses and tumblers, a bottle of wine and perhaps a can of lager. Then he would sit down and lounge with his legs crossed, an arm placed languidly along the back of the seat and his cap tilted back. He didn't drink. The bottles were most likely empty, but he enjoyed sitting there, admiring the comings and goings of people and cars, giving a little royal wave or nod when the mood took him.

Scobae's life was like a ray of sunshine on a depressing day. His escapades brought pleasure to many and harmed none. Few of us can claim that. When he died his funeral was one he would have enjoyed and been proud of. Hundreds turned out to give thanks for his time on earth. A lot of joy was lost from the life of the town when Scobae passed away.

In Ballynure

The little stone building, belonging to the Church of Ireland (Christ Church), is used by the local people as a meeting place for all sorts of things. The weekly dance, run by Andy and Jean to raise money for the church and charity is one such event.

Across the narrow road and opposite the small hall is an ancient graveyard, quiet and peaceful it sits almost surrounded by ivy clad trees. A low moss covered dyke, on the roadside, rises to knee height as stones stop level with the grassy sward, which leads round to one corner, where there is a heavy black iron gate. Beside this is a stone stile to allow easy access to the other side of the gate, to the other side sits a low stone building, once used to keep bodies until they were of no use to grave robbers.

Pristine in winter under a blanket of snow or hoar frost, in spring it bursts into life, first with a carpet of snowdrops underneath the bare branches and dark Irish yews, followed by gaily coloured crocuses, glowing against the time weathered head stones and later with the bursting buds of the hawthorn, beech and forsythia, rising above a sea of daffodils, it is, if anything, more beautiful than many a well tended garden .

It was one of those late summer evenings when the gloaming lies gently on the countryside. On that particular night, as the summer evening darkened, the only bright colour was in the wild flowers and the old fashioned scented roses, scrambling haphazardly over the remains of what could have been a cottage, but is really the ruins of an old church, once preached in by Jonathan Swift, which sits in the centre of the graveyard. The yews tell of a pagan past, thousands of years before Christianity claimed the site.

The hall was hot and my dress a bad choice for the time of year, so to cool down I stepped outside into the quiet night. The music drifted on the air and across the winding road to where the stones, with their many names, stood, as though listening to the lilting melodies. As I watched, a soft mist fell over everything. Suddenly the mist twisted into floating shapes, moving and curling as though dancing to the music being played in the hall.

Before my incredulous, disbelieving eyes, these forms became men and women, children, mothers with babies in their arms. Some watched the others dancing, while children played ring-a-ring-a-roses. Here and there lovers stood, entwined in each other's arms – all oblivious to my presence – all that is save one, who looked my way, held my gaze and nodded a greeting, as she placed her finger on her lips, indicating silence.

"Are you coming in?" My dancing partner appeared in the doorway. Looking over towards the graveyard he nodded, "Quiet over there isn't it." Realising he could see only the head stones I replied, "Yes isn't it. I'll be in in a minute."

Among the graves the revellers stood silent, watching me, waiting for my response. "Your secret's safe with me," I whispered and smiled. With a little wave I turned towards the music filled hall, with the lady's "Thank you" wafting towards me, they were left to enjoy the melodies as we each returned to our own time and place.

When the dance ended we came out into the darkness of the summer night. Across the road the only movement was the moths, flitting silently from rose to rose, under the starlit sky. Had I imagined it all? Who can tell?

Tomorrow I would return and read the names on the moss covered stones.

A Parents' Gift

Me da he was a travellin' man,
He whittled pegs all day.
I never went to any school
An' copyin' him was play.
Me ma she'd go round all the fairs
To trade the goods he'd made'
We knocked on doors to sell our wares
'Til the sun began to fade.

Life was hard, our old stone shack
Was the only home I knew,
But laughter, love and happiness
Filled it through and through.
'Til one sad day, when on ma's brow
A heavy frown appeared.
Me da was ill, we waited,
Then came the news we feared.
With shoulders bowed in mourning,
We walked through Autumn leaves,
Me ma, she hugged da's raincoat
And never ceased to grieve.
Within a month she joined him,
I trudged alone through snow.
This time I hugged the raincoat,
Wondering which way to go.

Nestling in the pockets
Was a clothes peg and a knife.

To ease my heart I whittled
As I had done all my life.
Then I painted smiling faces
On heads I'd made of clay,
And baked them in the oven,
And knew where my future lay.

Folk loved my happy people,
The pegs sold far and wide.
I had to take on extra help,
Good luck was on my side.
So now I live in a grand house,
With paintings on the wall,
But pride of place will always go,
To the raincoat that hangs in the hall.

Youthful Infatuation

There is, of necessity, a certain callousness in youth.
Perhaps this is nature's way of helping us through the
bumps and bruises we all have to cope with on the path
to adulthood. Falling in love is one of the delights or
afflictions of growing up. When we are very young the
purity of the untutored mind is a wonder to watch. A
four year old and a five year old, holding hands almost
brings a tear to the eye.

Teenage years can be difficult and the feeling of love
can be a fickle thing. We see someone from a distance and

in our heads we decide we fancy them, so we watch out, hoping to see the object of our dreams and imagine them asking us out or even speaking to us. Years ago girls would never have thought of even asking a boy for a dance, never mind asking them out on a date. Men did the chasing, but even catching sight of the object of our desire was enough to keep the flame of hope alive. This, can it even be called a crush, lasted for a few days or weeks, until at last the dreamboat headed in our direction. Alas he was too late. You had already transferred your affection to yet another god-like being.

Sometimes an admirer could become more persistent and the result was you had, what would now be called a stalker. Jimmy was one of these. He haunted the one he'd set his heart on. Anywhere she was he was there in the vicinity with his trusty push bike. Whenever she stepped out of her front door, he and his trusty bike just happened to be passing. Sadly for him he was not even on her radar. When she realised what he was doing she tried hard to cope and put him off without being hurtful.

We, his friends, tried to dissuade him. This seemed only to make him try harder to win her affection. The two of them, he and the bike, which he never seemed to ride but walked along beside, guiding it with a nonchalant grace, by placing one hand on the centre of the handlebars, were constantly where ever she was. We began to think he couldn't ride the thing but instead used it as a companion or mate.

After coming off the last bus from Belfast one winter's night, as she walked up from the bus station in the blackness (at that time there were no street lights after ten o'clock) he and his trusty friend appeared from one of the many entries in the town. This nearly scared her to death and in shock, with a sinking heart she said, "Oh no. Not you again". Eventually Jimmy got the message of "Sorry no interest."

He picked up the pieces of his broken heart and three weeks later switched his love to another girl. This time he had better luck. The pair got married. Thank goodness he had a best man and not a bike standing beside him in the church. The marriage was a happy one. He turned out to be a loving and considerate partner and father to their son. They were never apart in all their years together and, when he died after thirty-four years of marriage, he was truly mourned and missed by his family.

Maggie

Maggie Barbour was one of those ageless people who never seemed to ever have been young and foolish, or to ever grow any older as time passed. She lived on the Ballyeaston Road in one of the long rows of terrace houses on the left hand side going up towards Ballyeaston.

Like many young men at that time, her brother and nephew, who lived with her, were involved in the local St. John's football team. This meant she, like other female relations and friends of the team, was drafted in when required to make sandwiches and pastry for visiting teams, committee meetings and of course the annual dance, which was held to raise funds for the team.

These dances were held in the Town Hall and were supported by those of somewhere near dancing age. This was anyone from the age of thirteen to those in their nineties, who could manage a whirl around the dance floor. These events were wonderful for keeping all generations in touch with each other through a common interest.

Maggie loved dancing. She was one of the old school, no rocking or jiving for her. She was strictly ballroom in the truest form. With a graceful, upright carriage, arms and hands always in the correct position she glided round the floor. No slouching or smooching was ever involved.

Maggie's hair, which was as dark as it could be without being jet black, was worn with a middle parting

and a neat, tidy roll round the nape of her neck, with never a hair daring to be out of place. She often made us children laugh as we listened to her and the other ladies talking about what they were going to wear on the night of the dance. At this time Maggie was about fifty-five years of age. Looking as though she was pondering a puzzling dilemma, she would say, "I'm not sure what to wear. I think I'll stick to my black or my black." Everyone smiled because Maggie never, at any time, wore anything other than black.

Some Dreams Come True

Ronnie was thirteen years old. The feelings of manhood were just beginning to stir and the one who caused the most mixed up emotions lived four doors away from his parents' house. Sally was five years older and at eighteen seemed to be from another world. She dressed in high heels, wore lipstick, went to dances and worked in Larne. Even without the added height of three inch heels she towered over him. While he worshipped her from afar she never even noticed the adoring looks of the small boy down the street.

As soon as he was old enough he joined the navy. Coming home as often as he could, he would linger at the front door hoping to see her as she passed by. Eight years went by. Ronnie met other girls and even got engaged to one but it did not work out.

His mother told him, in one of her letters, of a terrible accident involving Sally and her parents. They were all seriously injured. It was thought that Sally would pull through but sadly no such hope was given of her parents, who clung to life for a short time then died within a day of each other. Ronnie's mother kept him up to date on Sally's progress back to full health and on how she was coping with the loss of both parents. Her boy friend, it appeared, wasn't made of strong enough stuff to offer a shoulder to lean on and walked away.

When the time seemed right, Ronnie wrote to Sally telling her of his sorrow at her loss and giving his best wishes for her progress. Not long after, he received a

letter back thanking him for his sympathy. They carried
on writing to each other for the next few months. When
he next came home, instead of lingering at his front door
hoping to see her, he plucked up his courage and
knocked on number twenty-three. Sally answered the
door and welcomed him in with a warm smile.

Now they met as equals. Ronnie was no longer the
uncertain, thirteen year old schoolboy. Instead he was a
young man, nearly six foot tall, confident and handsome,
proudly wearing his navy best.

They shared almost every day of his leave, talked and
laughed and occasionally he held her when she wept.
Then almost before they knew what was happening, they
realised they were in love.

Ronnie's time in the navy was almost over. As soon as
possible after he returned, they married and settled down

to life together. The years passed with the usual mixture of family life, the joy of children being born, the worry when they were ill, the ups and downs, the tears and laughter, celebrations and funerals. Whatever life threw at them they faced together, their faith in one another never faltering.

Now here they were at another celebration with children, grandchildren, relatives and many friends gathered together. The speeches, all of them light-hearted and funny, were over. Ronnie stood up to bring things to a close. He didn't try to outdo any of the previous speakers. Instead he said exactly the right thing. After thanking everyone for being there to help them celebrate fifty happy years together he said, "I wouldn't have missed how our lives turned out for all the world." Then lifting his glass, his eyes meeting Sally's, his toast was, "To Love."

A Cure for Loneliness

I was feeling I needed some company.
I was lonely and wanted a yarn.
So I went out to the farmyard
And entered into the barn.
I said "Hello" to the cattle
And the hens came runnin' round.
I forgot the place was slippy,
So I landed on the ground.

The postman saw me lyin',
Legs sprawled and skirts in the air.
He lifted me up and I kissed him, 'Thanks'
But he ran off in a scare.
Now I know I'm no beauty, but
Surely I'm not that bad.
So I had a look in the mirror
Oh, the vision I saw was sad,
I felt like runnin' and hidin'
And curling up in bed,
But I gave myself a shake, it was
My own fault when all's said.
So I gathered my thoughts together,
Said I, there are don'ts and dos,
Don't stay in your comfy slippers,
Put on yer high heeled shoes,
And hook yerself into some corsets
Even if you can't breathe.
Then head for a singles location,
It's time for a man I believe.

Squeeze your fat rolls into your wee black dress,
The one that stretches a bit.
If you sit at a table and suck in your gut
It'll still look as if it's a fit.
Some fun you need, I told myself.
You'll get none sittin' lone on the shelf.
The only company you'll find there, is the
Blue and white cracked delph.
I piled on the make-up, mascara, rouge and gloss,

And if there's some don't like it
I reckon that's their loss.
As I backcombed my hair and piled it all up,
I chewed on some nougat and it kinda got stuck.
So out came the dentures and I
Scrubbed them all clean.
I put them back in and I looked like a dream,
When the lippy gloss was topped up once again.
Then I got in the car and made off down the lane.
There were the men, thin, fat, scruffy and neat.
The organ played loud and I grabbed me a seat.
A nice man approached and we had a drink or two.
Well one thing led to another and the time it just flew.
Then he whispered to me, "I think we two
Could have a good time. What about you?"
Well!!!
You could have knocked me down with a feather.
My brain cells were whizzing round hell for leather.
It had been so long I'd forgotten what to do.
But I'd read 'The Perfumed Garden' and
'The Kama Sutra' too.
So I accepted his kind invitation
And wow! We've had so much fun
Using our imagination, since
Our 'Grand Time' begun.

An Unexpected Gift

People come into each other's lives accidently. Often because of reputation, fictional or fact, they are folk we would not normally get to know.

Years ago when our children were small, Derek, my husband, played a lot of football. As you know, when a sport is involved it's a case of 'We're all mates together'. One of the fellas in the team had been in and out of prison a few times for minor theft, never violence, just stealing. Oh I know you are saying that's bad enough but I'm simply explaining the way things were. He was often in our home for a bite to eat, before and after his spells inside. With us he was as honest as the day is long and I never had any doubt in trusting him.

I'll tell you about an event that happened and how it was coped with and you can think about what you would have done. We were having a cup of tea and Dave (not his real name) had joined us. We were talking about things we'd like to do. I said I'd like to cover my furniture but as material was so expensive it would have to do the way it was.

Nothing more was mentioned about it. However late one evening the door got a knock. When I answered it there was Dave, holding a bale of bright red tartan material. He said, " I thought this might be of some use to you " and shoved it into my surprised arms. What to do? Was it even legal? I didn't want to hurt him by saying no, but all the while my brain was whizzing with all sorts of questions – like, is this a knock-off or did he come by it in his job or – or — ? Whatever! The bright red

tartan ended up inside our house. The idea of a whole suite covered in the material was off putting to say the least, and it wasn't really welcome to stay. So what was to be done?

The solution to me seemed simple. I lived in an estate where there were dozens of children from three to eight years old. The brainwave was to get my granny's old treadle sewing machine out and make the whole bale into little pinafore dresses and trousers. These I shared round all the families with children.

You see I'd decided that if, by the faintest of chances, the getting of the tartan was questionable, then the police would have a lot of work on their hands trying to sort things out. Mind you it was funny to look out and see a dozen children out playing, all dressed in red tartan. Where ever it came from it was good quality. It washed like a ribbon and when those kids grew out of the little garments they were handed on. Recycling at its best.

Was I wrong? Maybe. What would you have done?

The Party

This was supposed to be a party. One of those selling parties I'd somehow or other been badgered into holding. You know the patter they use to shame you into doing this. It's, if you hold a night, your friend (the one holding the party you are attending) will be able to get such and such a thing for half price or even free. They make it sound as if it would be downright selfish of you not to do so.

Having gained my consent, however unwillingly given, I'm told that all I have to do is supply a cup of tea and a biscuit. Ha! If only. Most of these parties are an excuse to show off beautiful homes and belongings as well as an expertise in the cookery department.

Now my home is my nest. It's, as granny would have called it, clean enough to be healthy and shabby (or is it dirty) enough to be homely. My cooking, as I've said before, is done because of necessity not in desire or love of it, so this party was something to be dreaded.

The time had come. I felt like a visitor in a room full of Hyacinth Bouquets. There they were sitting round my living room, taking in every grain of dust, each cobweb, every smear on the window pane and every stain on the carpet. The sandwiches were well filled and the tray bakes were passable but making coffee really worried me.

Even buying a coffee in a cafe these days is a mine field. It seems easy. "I'll have a coffee please". "What sort?" They look at me as though I'm an idiot, who has been let out for the day.

"What have you got?" This is met with a tut and a bored, can't be bothered look as they point to a list behind the counter. Ye Gods. The haze of print is no help as I've left my glasses at home.

I say, "Just give me a plain, ordinary coffee."

"Small, medium or large?" again with that witheringly bored look.

"Small, please" I tell her, beginning to feel the whole ordeal is not worth the trouble, especially when the mug of coffee is not much better than dish water.

So here I am asking if anyone is ready for coffee. "Yes please", comes a chorus. Then it's "I'll have a latte, a mocha, an Americano, a cappuccino, an espresso and on and on. In the end I hold up my hand. "Sorry. It's instant or you can have a cup of tea."

Then come the questions – is it green? herbal? Indian? China?

I laugh and say, "That's instant too."

Is it an Age Thing?

When we are children we store things up in our minds like squirrels with nuts. We forget very little, especially if we've been promised a treat, but then we have not a lot in our minds to confuse us.

When we acquire a few more decades in age and hundreds of memories to sort out, we may forget things or take a moment or two to recall some past events. Much to the amusement or annoyance of children and grandchildren, names get confused. The young ones look at us, shake their heads and raise their eyes in exasperation, with that pitying look that says, 'they're at that age when they're heading towards their dotage'. So is it an age thing? Some, especially the young, say that it is. But is that the reason we mislay things and lose keys and glasses? I refuse to believe that. Surely it's because, as we get older, we have so much on our minds that we only half think about what we are doing.

For instance, there you are in the middle of baking or cooking the evening meal when the phone goes off so you hurry to answer it. It's your best friend with some juicy gossip about someone who's got too big for their boots, being brought down to the same level as everyone else. So you forget about what you were doing, until the blue smoke and the stench of burning has you racing into the kitchen.

Damn! When the oven was turned on, the fact that the remains of last night's chicken and the carving knife, with the plastic handle, were still inside, had been

forgotten. After flapping a tea towel everywhere it's back to the cooking.

Now where did I leave that square of margarine? It's not in the kitchen. You remember it was in your hand when you answered the phone. There it is dripping down the radiator cover. You grab the first thing that comes to hand and frantically start wiping the greasy surface. Then you realise the rag in your hand, now oozing with gunge, is in fact your newly laundered favourite blouse. In panic you rush back into the kitchen. As you do so, you slip on some marg that has dripped on to the floor. Down you go, banging your head on the wall. In the middle of seeing stars you hear a voice and think that you are hallucinating.

The voice asks, "Are you alright? Are you still there? Is something wrong?"

Through the mist of pain you remember that the person on the other end of the phone is still holding on.

But no, forgetfulness is not an age thing. It's too much clutter in our minds, too many things to contend with. What is needed is a few days pampering, a holiday and of course a new blouse. Sadly life will go back to its usual confusion. All your memories will be alive and well, all fighting to jump into your mind. But don't let anyone ever tell you that forgetfulness is an age thing.

Spirits

I've a question for you. Do you believe in ghosts or spirits, or do you give no thought to unexplained happenings? I would describe myself as sceptical and yet things happened in our house I have no way of explaining.

We lived in a newly built house from the time the children were born until they were in their late teens. They were very young when strange things started to happen. Heavy footsteps were heard running across the upstairs bedrooms. This was happening when the whole family were sitting round the living room fire.

At first things were put down to wind or weather, or

leaving a window open causing a door to bang. These
things were checked out and found not to be the cause.
Then we blamed our imagination. This didn't work
however, because the living room door began opening
and closing by itself.

Who, what and why? were the questions we asked
each other. No answers came. To stop the children being
afraid or frightened as they got older, and to make things
more normal, the 'whatever it was' was given the name
'Oscar'. When noises or feet were heard running round
the bedrooms, or when doors opened and closed for no
reason, we would say, "There's Oscar having fun".
Whatever it was seemed to mean us no harm so we
accepted its presence. We told no one about it. It's not
really the sort of subject you can drop into an everyday
conversation.

My sister-in-law, Valerie knew nothing about these
events. She was baby- sitting for the first time and
looking forward to having the children to herself, so off
we went knowing they were in safe hands. We arrived
home four hours later to find her white as a sheet and
absolutely terrified. Oscar had been up to his tricks again.

Valerie would visit when we were there, but never again would she sit on her own.

This continued all through the years of the family growing up. Things didn't happen all the time, though they often caused annoyance when they did. Oscar began to enjoy hiding things. A bread knife for example, would be found months later on top of an upstairs wardrobe. When hiding things, wallets and purses were the favourite targets.

One Saturday morning our son was going to Belfast. He left his wallet on his pillow while he showered and dressed. When he turned to lift it there was no wallet. We searched every corner of the room. We even stripped and remade the bed. The missing wallet could not be found, so off he went to Belfast with borrowed money. An hour or so later I went upstairs and looked into the room. There on the pillow of the remade bed, lay the wallet – plain for all to see.

Oscar began to get a bit braver. One morning both children woke at different times, but each, when they sat down to breakfast said that their face had been stroked during the night. When our daughter was about eight years old she told of seeing 'a wee man with a hat' at the bottom of her bed. She was the only one to see anything.

The children were used to strange occurrences. Though once, when our son was home from college in London, he was 20 years old at the time, he came downstairs and he was shaking. "Mum," he said, "I was in the bathroom and heard a noise behind me. I thought it was you but Oscar spoke my name and touched me on the shoulder."

One day my aunt was standing beside me in our tiny kitchen. She was a down-to-earth Ulster woman, who scoffed at any talk of ghosts and such. I was washing out three flasks, the tops of which were placed beside us on the kitchen bench. When I reached for the tops there were two instead of three. One had vanished. "But", Rhena said, "Where did it go? We haven't moved from here or opened any doors or cupboards. How can it not be here?"

The flask top turned up a few days later at the back of a drawer in the bedroom.

Whenever I was in the house on my own, Oscar was at his most active. One morning after tidying up, before going into Ballyclare for shopping, I checked what money was in my purse. I set it on the bench and filled the kettle to make a cup of coffee before heading out. When I turned to reach for it, the purse had disappeared. "Oh, Oscar, come on, not today" I moaned. Now this may seem strange, but I often had one sided conversations with my uninvited resident. The kettle had boiled so I made the coffee and went into the living room to drink it. My bottom had scarcely touched the sofa when the cupboard doors in the kitchen began to bang.

For a minute or two this was ignored, but, as though to attract my attention, the doors opened and closed louder and faster. I spoke without moving, "Oscar, please give me my purse. I need to buy food and all the money I have is in it." The banging stopped so I went back into the kitchen, hoping to see the missing purse, replaced where I had left it. I was disappointed. The counter top was white and the purse was black, so if it was there it ought to have been obvious. Just in case, for some reason, I wasn't seeing it, I decided to wash the bench from end to end, reasoning that if it was there, then the wash cloth would hit it.

All to no avail, the purse was not there. Nearly in tears I returned to the sofa. The banging started again. "Please, Oscar, I really have nothing to buy food with if you don't give up the purse." The cupboards stayed closed. I ventured into the kitchen once again. There it was, a black leather purse sitting on a newly washed white bench.

When the family grew up I was often on my own through the night. Many times I woke to hear heavy breathing and something softly stroking my face. Sometimes a heavy weight seemed to walk up my body. Very unsettling when you are alone in the house, though there was no feeling of danger. I had watched many of those stupid movies when a cross is used to cure things and save the day, so I decided that was what I would do. Did it help? Not in the least!

Like most families we discovered we needed more space and decided to move house. Would Oscar come with us? Our new house stayed peaceful and normal, though strangely I missed the unexpected happenings. Oscar seemed not to bother the new owner. He was a man on his own so maybe of no interest.

There are those who say that having a young girl in the house can sometimes cause strange things to occur. I have no explanation. We lived with things as they happened and they didn't do us a bit of harm.

Annie

Annie was a quiet, unassuming person who usually let things flow over her head. Folk could scream and shout about the problems with politics, religion, the price of tea or how many fewer biscuits there were in a packet than there once were, and Annie held her tongue.

"Things will happen anyway" she said. "Ordinary run of the mill plebs like us aren't listened to."

Of the crowd up on the hill at Stormont, all she would say was, "The lunatics are running the asylum."

Her mode of dress was like her home, neat and well

kept. She wore pleated skirts with ladylike blouses and cardigans or soft coloured twin sets. Her neat, grey hair was always short and curled.

Annie was very particular about her space of the cribben which she brushed at least twice a day. We children were always getting disapproving looks for chalking hopscotch on her bit of pavement, so she wasn't very popular with those of us involved in these activities.

One day Annie was brushing the remains of our game on to the road when a local bully appeared. We children kept our heads down trying not to attract his attention. A little cat was curled up on one of the door steps. The bully crossed the street and was just about to kick the sleeping kitten when he got a bang on the back of his knees as Annie whacked him with her brush, knocking him off his feet.

This virago of a person we'd never seen before kept poking and pushing with her yard brush until he picked himself up and took off. As we onlookers stood frozen in shock, Annie simply shook her head and said, "Some things are worth fighting for." We children were full of admiration and treated Annie with a new found respect. From then on we stopped drawing on her cribben.

We learned something that day. There are indeed some things worth standing up for and most bullies are cowards at heart.

A Wedding

Stories of folks lives are much more interesting than any made up tales. One night at a dance in the country I was sitting beside a woman, known to me only by sight. We chatted for a few minutes before she said, "You write don't you?" Wondering what was coming next I nodded.
"Well", she continued "I've a story you might be interested in but if you use it don't use our names".
Fascinated I agreed. This was her story.

My daughter and her boyfriend were engaged for three years and decided to get married in the next year. The following months were spent in a whirl of organising cars, photographs, cake and invitations, to say nothing of choosing material and colours for the bridesmaids' dresses and the bride's own dress. Then there were the fittings, the men's outfits, the reception venue and what to have to eat. Flowers, rings, honeymoon destination and speeches were talked about over and over again. Every detail was discussed and re-discussed. The church and music were the easy bits.

We were worn out by the time the wedding day arrived. All the parties before hand had exhausted us, so we breathed a sigh of relief when we were all dressed and ready to leave for the church. Our daughter came downstairs looking so beautiful her father and I had tears in our eyes.

When we arrived at the church there was a bit of a commotion. Everyone was flustered. The groom had not arrived. The car drove around to give him more time but when it came back he still hadn't appeared, and he didn't. The wedding was off. We all went back home. Our daughter took off her lovely gown, folded it up and placed it back in its box and that was it.

"What did you do?" I asked because I was horrified. "Did you not feel like smashing his head in?"

"I was so embarrassed and so worried about my daughter that I couldn't even go out of the house for weeks. I didn't want to talk to anyone in case they would ask questions", she replied.

"Well what about your daughter? She must have been in a state."

"She took the time planned for the honeymoon to get herself together and just carried on. We all did the same." She shook her head, "What else could we do?"

"Did your daughter meet someone else or was she scared to trust another man?" I questioned.

"Oh that was thirty years ago. Although it was heart wrenching, she is now happily married with two lovely grown up children. She married quietly, three months after that fateful day, in a registry office wearing a simple suit, with only the close family in attendance. This time the groom was waiting. This time without all the pressure he had managed to overcome his nerves.

I wonder how many times down the years the story was told with a little sting in the tail or how many girls would have given him a second chance.

Jane's War

This tells the tale of my grandmother's experiences during the Great War.

My Jimmy's a lovely kindly man,
He'd hurt no-one and help where he can.
But for war the government had a plan,
To volunteer with others he ran.
They said it would last a month or two,
But time went by and before we knew
A world at war met our horrified view,
Our leaders words we found untrue.

I cared for the weans and to make ends meet
Made clothes and turned each torn sheet
Into nappies, aprons and night gowns, to keep
The money to buy shoes for growing feet.
In our plot I grew cabbage, spuds and peas.
The hedgerows provided their berries for free,
An apple, a damson and cherry tree
Provided fruit for the neighbours and me.

We heard of the mud, the bombs and the gas.
We longed for the post, yet hoped he would pass.
Captain or private, death knows no class,
And no news was good news for each wife and lass.
The letter came! With quaking heart
I dreaded the news it would impart.
MISSING IN ACTION it said, and a dart
Of terror tore my world apart.

Another letter said he'd been found.
In fact he'd crawled, wounded from enemy ground.
The bullet removed, recovered and sound,
They sent him back for another round.
A later letter said, INJURED IN BATTLE.
The newspapers cried, with angry rattle
Of heroes used as though mere chattel
Tossed like fodder to hungry cattle.

At last it was over, home they came
The damaged in mind, the blind, the lame.
The able bodied though glad, felt pain
For those they would never see again.

We started to build our lives once more.
Women who'd worked on the factory floor,
Went back to the home. Prospects were poor
For men searching for work, their spirits sore.

Men who had fought for freedom's sake
Looked at the life that had come in the wake
Of battle and asked, "Why can we not take
Some good from the victory we helped to make?"
Where was the freedom they'd fought for and won?
For the rich and the powerful life was fun,
But when would the masses bask in the sun?
The war for equality had just begun.

Don't You Dare

*This is a story of our time, related to me by a mother, pushed to
the very end of her tether.
I didn't dare use their real names.*

Kathleen was fit to be tied. Her son had pushed her to the
limit. She couldn't think where she had gone wrong with
Mike. Her other two boys had never given her any
trouble. Now here was this brat making up for both of
them.

He was always borrowing money, which of course he
never paid back. She realised he was all take, take, take.
This was the final straw. Her patience snapped.

"I told you not to have the dammed thing done in the

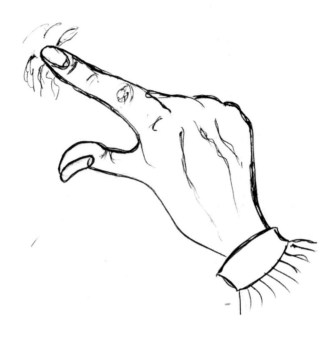

first place" she raged, "but oh no, you had to be the big guy. How much did it cost? Now don't try to bluff me. Tell me the truth".

"WHAT! Ninety pounds for that! You must be mad. Hang on a minute. Where did you get the money from? Sure you're 'signing on'. You only have about sixty quid a week coming in. Is that where the money you borrowed from me went? All that cash to walk round with a devil's head on the back of your neck. Well I'm not giving you any more money, so when you hate it you'll be stuck with it, or pay to have it removed from your own pocket."

Mike opened his mouth to speak but didn't get a chance.

His mother, who was on a rant, held up her hand and carried on with her tirade, "Stop right there. Don't you dare tell me the NHS will pay for it. You haven't paid a penny into the health service and there's your grandfather waiting for a new hip for over a year, after all the money he's paid in all his working life. Who do you think you are that you should be lifted and laid all your lazy lay-about life? Get out of my sight before I do something I'll regret".

This was one request that Mike was glad to obey. He kept hoping she would calm down as she'd always done before, but this time Kathleen's back bone stiffened. From that day on he was left to swing by his own tail.

It was a wake-up call, late but effective. Sometimes growing up takes a very long time.

Mary's Magical Memory

Sitting at the bedside of a lady in her late eighties she began to speak of her childhood. Her parents had lived in a stone cottage on the outskirts of the then village of Ballyclare. There was no electric light nor was there a supply of water piped into the house. The water came from a well in the field across the lane and the home was lit by oil lamps and candles.

Mary was an only child. There were no close neighbours so she spent a lot of time on her own. She laughed when asked if she was ever lonely. "Never" she replied. "Sure I had the chickens, dog and cats to play with". Then giving me a sidewise look she said,"And I had my secret friends to play with." When questioned about this she smiled and told this tale.

All day long the candle sat unnoticed in the corner of the room while sunlight streamed through the small window, giving the room a golden glow. Once the gloaming began to creep in through the self same window, eager hands lifted the candle and placed it on the table in the centre of the room. A taper was lit from the turf fire, whose warmth was already permeating the small space. The taper touched the candle wick and a tiny flickering flame was born. Inside a few seconds it had strengthened and proudly cast its light around the darkening room.

Mary said that when she was seven years old this was her favourite time of the day. While her mother prepared the evening meal in the kitchen and before her father arrived home, she sat quiet and alone, waiting. She watched the candlelight as it danced about the room. Only she knew this was the time the fairies came out to play and the game they loved most of all was hide and seek.

They'd run and hide behind the heavy furniture or under the cushions and disappear into the shadows. Sometimes they would flutter, on tiny gossamer wings, to the top of the pictures, ornaments and curtains, giving tiny tinkling screams of laughter and delight as they played.

Mary gave them all names according to how they appeared when she first saw them. There was Sweetpea who always smelt delicious, Happy with his wonderful

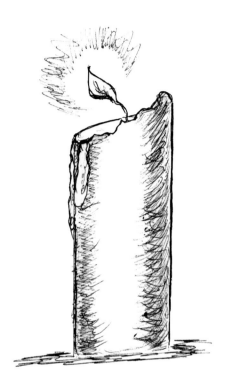

smile, Gingle because of the jangling of her coloured beads, Russet with his auburn hair and Sky with her floating blue dress. There were some who seldom appeared and others who came nearly every evening.

How she loved the time they shared but it was all too brief. In far too short a time her mother would call out to

Should she be feeling a little sad they gathered round, dancing and singing to make her feel better. Sometimes they whispered secrets into her ear as they sat on her shoulder. Recalling these times Mary's eyes lit up. "Do you know" she said, "I can still hum the tune they taught me".

How she loved the time they shared but it was all too brief. In far too short a time her mother would call out to say the evening meal was ready. At the sound of a grownup's voice the tiny visitors disappeared back into Fairyland, where they would stay until another gloaming meant that the candle was lit once more and once again magic would fill the room.

There are those who will decry this as a silly fanciful tale. Others will perhaps, like me, feel a pang of envy and wish that they too could be able to carry the wonderful imagining of childhood through all their adult life and even, like Mary, be able to hum a secret tune.

Friends

Sarah sat in silent rage listening to her favourite singer singing one of those songs, full of poor me, pitiful lyrics so beloved by girls in their early teens. Her bedroom was a tip. In a fit of temper she had torn her magazine and thrown it, her stuffed animals and anything else that wasn't nailed down all over the place, trying to vent some of her rage and calm down.

"The bitch" she thought. Even in her mind she couldn't bring herself to put a name to the person she had called her best friend for all of her sixteen years. They had played together as children. Living next door to one another they often slept over in each other's home.

Had she but known, in another bedroom, Jill, her one time friend was doing exactly the same as she was. "How could she?" she asked herself, thinking back on their last conversation.

Shane had walked by and winked as he did so, leaving the pair giggling in teenage excitement.

"Oh" Jill had told her friend, "I really like him and I think he likes me".

"No he doesn't", Sarah snapped back. "You know rightly when he waved over at me last week that I fancied him and he liked me. He never waved at you".

Jill retaliated, "I wasn't there when he waved. You told me about it later on. Maybe he wasn't waving at you and anyway I've as much right to go out with him as you do".

"No you don't. I said it first so it's hands off", Sarah hit back in indignation.

"Hands off yourself, you selfish cow", Jill shot at her and turned away into her own house.

That had been two days ago. Tonight was the Youth Club and usually the pair went together but not tonight. Coming out of their front doors the two caught sight of each other and glared. Just then Shane, the object of their difference and desire, came on the scene but he was not alone. Laura was with him and he had his arm around her waist.

Imagine! The cheek of him, leading the girls on, when he was already spoken for. Pride came to the rescue. As the love-birds passed both Sarah and Jill said, "Hi ya" with bright wide smiles.

"Well!" said Sarah when the pair were out of earshot, "What does he think he's doing? Look at her. She has no fashion sense. What's she like?"

Jill, equally disgusted, exclaimed, "I can't believe it. You're so much more attractive than she is".

Sarah shook her head in disbelief, "Well, so are you. I thought he had a bit of sense".

"Ugh", Jane replied, "He's an idiot. Sure if he had any sense he'd see straight through her. She's a bit of a tart."

Sarah linked her arm through Jill's, disagreements forgotten, stuck her chin in the air and said in a smug tone, "That was a lucky escape. We're well rid of him".

Off they went, united in their disgust of Shane and in the enjoyment of tearing poor Laura's character to shreds.

Belfast

The cranes and gantries stood tall against the sparkling
sea.
Sunshine lit the soft green hills around Belfast,
Through the early morning gloom covering mill and
factory.
Like the glistening of tears in a veil of pity,
An eerie mist clung to the saddened city.

Yesterday the streets were bright with music, colour and
song,
Laughing people greeted one another.
Along the celebrating streets the cheerful throng
Through church and pub and chapel drifted in and out,
No thought of creed or flag was anywhere about.

Today the only colour in the street is blood drenched red,
The only music, beats from muffled drum,
Our songs are dedicated to the dead.
And time, with heavy tread walks slowly by,
While tired, once happy streets ask the question, WHY?

Tomorrow, Ah tomorrow, What dreams can we share?
The future waits, as angry words are tossed.
Our vain hopes fade – yet listen, somewhere, unaware,
Children innocently chant a skipping ditty,
Belying the eerie mist, clinging to the city.

A Bloody Incident

Friday night at 10pm I headed upstairs, had a lovely shower and washed my hair. Shiny clean, dressed in pyjamas and dressing gown, it was back downstairs on bare feet to get comfortable, ready for the movie on TV.

I'd been sewing a zip into a skirt, so needles and scissors were still lying around. As I sat down the phone rang. It was my son calling from America. We began a lovely chat. Then I remembered that I'd meant to turn the washing machine on. I got up but after a few steps something hit my toe. Looking down I saw the scissors sticking out of my large toe (big toe makes it sound funny and honestly, it certainly was not).

"Oh my goodness", I cried out loud.

"What's wrong ?" asked the voice on the phone.

"I've got scissors stuck in my foot. Hang on till I pull them out. Good Lord!" or words to that effect, I exclaimed as with a tug the scissors came out and so did the blood.

"What is it? What's going on?" Gary wanted to know.

"I'm bleeding all over the place. There's a shoe here. I'll put it on so that I don't mess everything up".

Again from the phone, "How bad is it?"

Looking down I saw that the blood was flowing out over the top of the shoe. My mind was thinking all sorts of things. Like is there an artery in the foot and if there is, where is it? (Alright so it sounds melodramatic).

"Mum, how bad is it?" the voice on the phone insisted.

"It's not too good. There is an awful lot of blood and it's not looking like stopping any time soon".

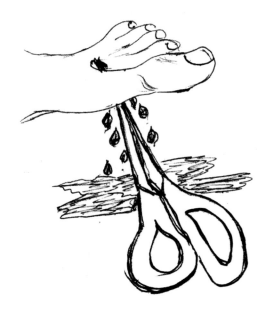

There was worry in Gary's voice, "Maybe you should phone for an ambulance".

"I am not going to phone for an ambulance", I said, trying to stay calm. All the while I was thinking, if it is an artery, how long have I got before I pass out and bleed to death. (Ok, so panic was not far away.)

"Mum, sit down and put your foot up high and put on a tourniquet".

"I'm going to do that. As soon as I get out of this shoe I'll tie a band round my ankle".

"Mum, tie around the base of your toe as well and phone for an ambulance".

"I am not phoning for an ambulance".

Pulling off the shoe full of blood, I hop across the room to the sofa, leaving a trail of blood behind. I fall onto the seat and put the offending foot up on a cushion on the puffee. I tell Gary that I am sitting down but will have to put the phone down to tie the ribbons around my foot.

This was no easy job. To tie a knot on an injured foot with blood covered hands is a bit awkward. Once the two ties were in place, I remembered the warning to loosen them every fifteen minutes to let some fluid through, otherwise gangrene could set in. (Alright, this may seem a bit over the top but it seemed perfectly logical at the time.)

"What's happening now, Mum?" asked the voice from America.

"Well I think it's slowed down a bit".

"Look if you aren't going to get an ambulance call Sheenagh".

"I'll do that if it doesn't stop soon".

"No, Mum, do it now. If you don't I will".

I rubbed my brow with my bloody hand and sat with the sticky red phone against my ear, "Alright, as soon as you put your phone down I'll ring her".

Knowing that he would call her and how given to exaggeration he was I rang my daughter. No answer- Great. Two minutes later the phone rang. "Sorry mum, I was in the bath. Do you want me to do something?" Keeping as calm as possible I explained what had happened .

"We'll be down as soon as we get some clothes on".

Five minutes later she arrived. By this time Gary was

back on the line. "Hang on. Sheenagh and Finn are just coming in".

The living room door opened unto a scene that looked as though a murder had been committed. Finn took one look at the red foot and hands, blood smeared face and hair, went as white as a sheet, nearly passed out and had to go back to the car.

"Mum", Sheenagh said in horror, "look at all that blood. It's lying in puddles"

Gary, meantime, 2000 miles away was hearing this conversation.

"It's not bleeding as much now", was related to him.

"I'll leave you now that Sheenagh's there. Be careful". The phone went dead.

From the kitchen, "What can I use to clean this up?"

"Use anything you can get your hands on in the towel cupboard and throw them out along with the shoes".

She could have used my favourite coat and I wouldn't have cared. Then it was time to get cleaned up and bandaged before the ubiquitous cup of tea.

After a few days limping around it was almost back to normal.

Let's hope it was a lesson learned. Put sharp objects safely away. But ....

A Summer Highlight

After a grey, wet, freezing winter the longed for summer was suddenly on us, stretching out ahead with the promise of weeks of sun and excitement. No holiday was planned for this year. As often happens, the events life presents, prevented the possibility of booking anything. Instead all the books I kept meaning to read, would be read. Long walks in my favourite places and days spent up our own North Coast, with the treat of a meal cooked by someone else, beckoned.

Alas for dreams. Wind, rain and cold weather put paid to all my hopes. Then along came the man on the white horse to save the day. Well, actually, it was Alice Andrew, who helps run the dancing group in Doagh. She suggested we go over to Edinburgh for the 'Tattoo'. This would only be for three days but the chance to escape was extremely welcome and we grabbed it with both hands.

We were picked up by bus in Doagh at 6.15am. Although we were leaving from Larne, the organisers had to pick up other trippers in Belfast, so we had the scenic route to the ship.

The journey over to Scotland was passed with good conversation and coffee. After getting off the ship and travelling for about an hour the coach stopped at Dobbies, a large garden centre with a wonderful restaurant. By this time we were beginning to feel the pangs of hunger. Dorothy, whom I was to share a room with, and I decided to each have a baked potato with all

the trimmings. The young man, from behind the counter, went to get us our meal but returned to say there were none ready as it was still too early.

He offered to do ours in the microwave if that would do, but it would take seven minutes. We smiled, nodding our agreement and went to collect our cups of tea and settled down to wait. About eight minutes later the man came out and said it would be another five minutes. Again we agreed. Ten minutes later he was back, shame faced and apologising. Apparently, they had, in his words, cremated our potatoes. Not only that, but the microwave had blown up. Would we like to order something else?

"Good Lord", I said to Dorothy. "We're only off the boat and already we're causing havoc".

While we were eating our toasted sandwiches the manager arrived with four enormous cream buns as an apology for keeping us waiting. We could manage only one bun. The others we devoured with a late night cup of tea in our room.

The rest of the weekend was a great success and the Tattoo was fantastic.

Remembering Our Teens

A group of us were having a look through some photographs of a time when we were in our teens. Lindy said, "Sweet sixteen! Was I ever that age?"

The rest of us groaned and agreed. It seemed and indeed was a lifetime ago. We had a lovely time recalling the innocence of our younger selves.

The talk turned to the clothes we wore and how as teenagers we wanted to be different. We all owned a black taffeta circular skirt although we did have many other styles of skirt. Circular ones were sometimes made up of patchwork. There were ones made four yards of material gathered or pleated and held at our 20-24 inch waists with cummerbunds or broad leather or elastic belts for emphasis.

Others had a slight flare or were so straight and tight that they had to be slipped down to go to the loo.

Not to be outdone, the boys also had the opportunity to be fashionable. There were three routes to go down.

Like peacocks, they could wear long drapes, in brightly coloured plain material with long black revers, shoestring ties and suede shoes with high crepe soles or leather ones with long pointed toes, which had a habit of turning up at the front. Hair was brillantined up at the top in a soft swirl and collar length at the back, with never a hair out of place. Rock and Rollers had slightly different forms of this hairstyle or crew cuts. Leather jackets with studs and zips and jeans and tee shirts were more to their taste. Boots were often worn, sometimes with thick one inch

heels. Boys who favoured neither of these looks wore
brogues or oxfords on their feet, and grey trousers and
sports jackets, with one or two slits at the back and shirts
and ties. Hair, worn in a James Dean style, was carefully
swept into place.

   We, girls, starched or sugared layers of net petticoats or
wore hoops to make our skirts sit out. The hoops were
great until they broke and we looked like broken
umbrellas walking around. All outfits were worn with
stretch or cotton gloves, usually white but sometimes in
pastel shades. Our feet were clad in shoes with stiletto or

kitten heels or flat ballet pumps. Vanity cases, bucket bags and clutches were favoured for holding our necessary comb, lipstick and powder. Long hair was sometimes worn in a French roll, bun or pony tail. When going dancing we dressed these with small artificial flowers or sparkly ornaments. Short hair was cut in the Italian boy, bubble cut or pixie style, like Audrey Hepburn.

We wore cheap, throwaway jewellery. Woolworth's sold slim bangles of silvery metal with backs of various colours. These cost only a few pence so every pay day we would buy a few. Some girls had as many as fifty dangling on each arm.

Dressed up to the nines, we teenagers, male and female, went out to meet the person of our dreams. An experience that often turned into a nightmare, but were we put off? Of course we weren't. It was off with the old and out again to seek the new. When you are a teenager hope is a constant companion.

Life Happens

My twenty-first birthday wasn't much fun.
In fact it was over before it begun.
We were just going to have a party at home,
All my relations and friends were to come.
Where we would put them I hadn't a clue.
They'd be crushed like sardines

And the air would be blue
When the fat women sat on the men's bony knees
Or they'd find a wee space
Into which they would squeeze.

The buns they were ready, iced and all,
The house was scrubbed clean,
for the folks who would call.
But alas and alack, Life reared his head,
A great uncle of mine was suddenly dead,
So all of the vittals, iced buns and cake,
Were taken from me and sent to the wake.
Now it wasn't one of those joyful dos,
Where folks can down a drink if they choose.
This was really quite a serious affair,
Where religion was floating round in the air.

My twenty-first was something I'd rather forget,
Just thinking about it makes me upset.

Remembering

This piece came about when a friend said he was leaving to take up a job in Australia. I began to wonder what memories would go with me if this situation presented itself.

I'll remember good conversations,
A bit of craic, a drink of stout,
A sudden burst of laughter
When a joke is thrown about,
The razor wit, the quick retort,
The "How's about ye mate?"
The ready smiles and yet and yet

I'll remember the blasts, then silence,
Long seconds of dust filled air,
Where death and pain and anguish
Merge with dark despair.
But hope is a dream to follow,
While peace is a hard plant to grow.
There may be stormy times ahead
And yet, and yet, I know

I'll remember neighbours kindness.
They were there at need or wake,
Lending chairs and china,
Bringing sandwiches and cake.
The friendly nod of the stranger
When passing on the street.
The ceilidh and the soiree
With sounds of tapping feet.

Scrubbed steps and floral gardens,
The greens of field and hill,
Bogs filled with whin and heather,
Glens, waterfall and rill,
Primroses and bluebells,
Violets, fuchsia, bucky rose.
The wave of sea on golden sand,
The rocks where the seaweed grows.

The misty blue of the mountains,
The myths, the loughs, the lakes
The rivers where the trout hides
Music the wild bird makes.
The breeze with scent of hawthorn,
The grass beneath my feet,
The festival of harvest,
These memories are to keep.
And yet, and yet there's anger
That cannot be denied.
While some would injure others
Our beautiful Isle is defiled.
And yet, and yet there's a beauty
That makes this a place apart.
The love of this land and her people
Will never leave my heart.

And the Winner is

When buying a ballot ticket the thought of winning is not uppermost in our minds. Really it is more like giving a donation to whatever cause the draw is supporting. Even though there is little chance of winning, if you are present when the tickets are being drawn, there is an element of excitement.

There you sit, with your green, yellow and pink tickets, hope fading as ticket after ticket is pulled from the pile in the plastic bag, advertising one of the local supermarkets. All the decent prizes are gone, all that is left are bottles of orange squash and packets of biscuits. Your hope of winning has decreased along with the value of the things on offer. The last winner is picked from the bag. Even before the number is called, you know it's not yours because it is the only colour of ticket you haven't got.

Tombola is every bit as bad. None of your numbers end in the one needed to win a prize. Other folk are winning hair dryers, booze and boxes of luxury

chocolates, while you sit there like a deflated balloon.

Let's hope that getting into heaven doesn't depend on the luck of the draw. If it does, an awful lot of us, when the winners are called, will be sitting there with the wrong number, or a ticket of the only colour not drawn from the bag. It might be a case of "and the winning ticket is GOLD, number ...". It doesn't matter about the number, the ticket is the wrong colour. So the winner is —. Anybody but us.

When we were children

Funny how, no matter how fit, well and young we feel, as we get older, the young and innocent, those of the tender years from toddler to teen, think of us as relics from a dim and distant past.

When families get together for birthdays, Christmas or the odd get-to-gather, they are inclined to drift into reminiscences of the past. Talk of schooldays shared, with cruel and often embittered teachers, who took their frustrations out on the pupils by the use of the cane. This draws disbelieving gasps of horror from those attending any form of education establishment.

"A cane? You mean they actually hit you?" they say with eyes opened wide with amazement .

"Yes", we reply, "and some of them really enjoyed doing it."

We told of the few who really loved the fact of being

able to grab the interest of those they taught, and who had an influence on the choices we made later in life.

One teacher I remember was Mr Abba. He was different from our other teachers in that he was English and had a more modern outlook than the ones we were used to. Once I remember in drawing class, he set a chair on top of his desk and told us to draw it. Everyone finished their drawings, some better than others. We were all shocked when he said that while the work was good, no-one had done as he had requested. He explained that we had all drawn a chair as we pictured it in our minds and not from the angle we saw when it was placed above our line of vision. A simple lesson but one that made me look at things in a different way.

We told of schoolrooms with a fire at one end, behind the teacher's desk, and how one lady teacher stood in front of the glowing fire, warming her skinny backside, while we children struggled to write with pen and nib, held between freezing cold fingers.

They listened in disbelief when we told them about the lavatories situated at the far end of the playground, a joy to journey to in the good weather, sheer misery in the rain and snow. Yes, we told them, they were flush toilets but there were no wash hand basins, and everyone was expected to go only at break or lunch time. In between this it was a case of crossing legs and hoping.

The talk turned to smells and how they brought memories flooding back. The scent of rushing through a knee high wild flower meadow, or the sharp greasy smell of vinegar and chips in Chippy Smith's, the tang of apple

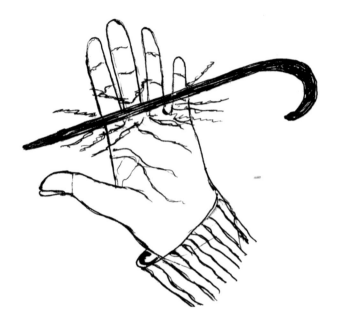

tarts or sweet clouty dumpling at Hallowe'en and the joy
of the clean smell of a bucket of kemp apples, bought
from a man at the front door. The appetizing aroma of
blackberry jam, bubbling up in a high saucepan, and the
excitement of waiting for a slice of buttered batch bread
loaded with the still warm jam, that would run down
your fingers, necessitating the pleasure of licking them
clean and the sharp fresh zing of orange and apple on
Christmas morning, in the toe of a stocking, not one of
those new fangled designer ones, just one of the grown-
ups socks or lisle stockings Strangely enough the one
smell we all had a memory of, was a hard- boiled egg,
mashed up in a cup with salt and pepper and a knob of
butter. And, we all agreed, it had to be in a cup.

One of the children always asks, "What sort of games

did you play, in ancient times, when you were young?"

Answers come from everywhere. "We played skipping on the road."

"Were you allowed? Did no-one ever get knocked down?"

We explain how in those days there was very little traffic, because few families had a car, so the roads became our playground. We told how the boys played football, cricket and trundle the hoop, while everyone played with perrie and whip, 'Pussy in the four corners', rounders, cowboys and Indians, truth or dare, hide and seek, marbles and conkers.

The girls played dressing-up and wee houses. We played ball against the walls of the houses, with two, three and sometimes four balls. We all drew hopscotch on the pavement and roller skated, while those who had bicycles, shared with the rest. Three pence, on Saturday afternoon, took us to the wooden benches at the front of the Reo picture house on Main Street, while with another three pence we could buy a chip or a bottle of Vinto.

Winter meant making icy slides, having snowball fights, rolling huge snowball to make snowmen and putting together makeshift sledges, using wheel less prams, old trays and scrap pieces of wood, bound together with bits of rope or long scraps of material. Then we'd spend many happy hours, trekking up the brae and round the corner at the top, before crowding, with no thought for safety, onto the ramshackle bases and careering down the hard packed slippery snow. We'd whizz down the steep hill, trying, often with no success,

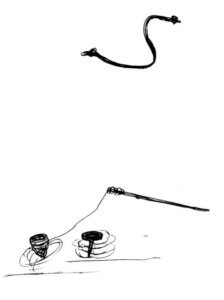

to control the curve at the bottom, which turns
downwards into the Ballycorr Road. Usually we ended
up in a sprawling, giggling heap at the side of the
cribben. Any hurt was ignored, loose snow was brushed
off and up the brae we'd go again, cheeks tingling, eyes
glowing with excitement. The only real danger, apart
from breaking an arm or leg, was falling into a pile of
snow covering horse droppings, but this too was brushed
off and taken in our stride.

   When the weather turned better we enjoyed walloping
flies with newspapers, rolled up into a sort of tube, as
they flew all over the dunkills (middens). We didn't
worry that they were full of household rubbish and
human excrement. Happy days were passed catching
bees in jam pots or building tents with worn out blankets,

curtains and anything else that could be nailed, tied and pegged out by broken brush shafts and any old bits of wood we found lying around.

The Craig Hill, with its quarries, sliding stone, hazel nuts and wild flowers and the Memorial Park and the meadows along the Sixmile were our playgrounds. Cattle were always grazing on the hills and meadows we played in, leaving their trademark pancakes behind them. If these were older, they crackled when stepped on, if they were fresh they squelched on and through our sandals and gutties.

Come to think of it, when you take in the pits, the cow claps and horse droppings everywhere we went, our lives were full of dung, one way or another.

Bob's Fireplace

There are fireplaces of all shapes and sizes, most of them more expensive than expected.

Once upon a time a circle of stones in the middle of a hut, built of woven willow, where smoke drifted up and all round the dwelling, seeping through the heather and moss filled cavity walls, sufficed. This may seem unhealthy to our pristine world, but it has been discovered that the smoke killed off many of the germs, much in the way antiseptic does today.

But back to my tale.

I once bought a dilapidated house and was looking

forward to doing it up. I knew exactly the kind of fireplace that would be perfect. The fireplace man lived at the Four Corners, just off the lower Rashee Road, a picturesque road, which runs past a wonderful old graveyard. Knowing exactly what I wanted, it was off to consult with Bob 'Robert' Sempy, who, in his younger days, had been a boxer. Standing about five foot eight or nine and as strong as an ox, with his high cheek bones, square chin, blue eyes and slightly off kilter nose, he presented a handsome presence. The front door was seldom used so it was up the side of the house and round to the back door.

"Come on in" said he, as he opened the kitchen door. I was ushered in and soon a cup of tea and a biscuit were set before me by his wife, a lovely woman, who enjoyed a bit of craic. All sorts of things were discussed before we got round to the fireplace.

They listened as I explained all about the dream I had and the reason for my visit. There were lots of ayes, nods and umms from man and wife. Eventually he and I journeyed over to his workroom. Fireplaces, great (no pun intended) and small, half finished and half built littered every space.

Picking my way carefully through the clutter, I pointed out materials I liked. I turned to Bob and asked, "Now you know exactly what I mean, don't you?"

"I do", Bob said sagely.

"Good", I replied.

Then the bold Bob dropped his bombshell, "but you're not going to get it"

Looking at him in astonishment I questioned, "Why not?"

"Because", said Bob, finger in the air for emphasis, "I don't think it would be right".

End of debate. Another fireplace was chosen and installed.

BOB WAS RIGHT. The one he suggested was perfect. It did in fact look GREAT - (this pun is intended)

A Modern Invention

The modern invention I most detest is the automated voice on the other end of the phone, with the words, "Listen carefully as this is meant to help you. Please press one for – press two for – and press three, four or five for –". When you do press a number it's on to another set of choices. All balderdash!

One of the problems it appears, is my accent. This is no

bother when speaking face to face, but obviously it is a problem to the automaton on the other end. "Sorry I did not understand. Say again." Or "Did you say three or eight? Please repeat." After the third or fourth repeat I bang the phone down and feel like stamping my foot as a four year old would do.

When will firms get the message? All we want is to speak to an actual person, preferably one we can understand and who understands us. We definitely don't want press one, two or three.

Someone phoned me the other day. He had a beautiful Scottish accent. He was from BT and wanted to see if I was on the best plan for me. He started to explain about their great deal for the internet. I stopped him by saying, "I haven't got and don't want the internet." This shocked him into silence. Then he told me of the fantastic deal I was already on, with discount for family and friends, any time calls, 1471 and 1571.

It all seemed wonderful. Not at all like the bills that I was paying, although I had all these benefits. I asked for a breakdown and he quoted prices. I asked if these were monthly or quarterly and why I should pay for 'family and friends' if any time calls are free. How come my bill is so high? The poor soul at the other end started ganching and got totally confused. I of course, at this stage, began to find the whole thing hilarious and started laughing.

This must have been infectious because the Scottish voice sounded amused as he said, "I think you're sending me up ". By this time the tears were running

down my cheeks as we both giggled.

"I bet you wish you hadn't rung me", I said.

He gave another laugh, "Well do you want me to call you again in three months to make sure you are happy?"

"If you feel up to it", was my reply, "but thank you for brightening up my day, and just so you know, I'm going to include this story in my next book."

He of course thought that this was a joke. I do hope he reads this and perhaps smiles at the memory of a foolish but surprisingly enjoyable few minutes of chat.

Love's Token

Just a small white pebble
Lying on the beach'
Shaped like a perfect loving heart
And close enough to reach.

He lifted this little treasure,
Pocketing it with pride,
Planning on bended knee to ask
His love to be his bride.

Proffering his little token
'Neath twilight laden skies,
He offered nature's trinket
Through true love's blinded eyes.

She spurned his pebble heart
With a toss of raven hair.
He stood alone in the starlight,
Wallowing in despair.

He set his seaside treasure
On the mantle for a year,
'Til he found his heartstrings singing
When a certain girl was near.

"How lovely," she smiled and picked it up.
"It's a perfect heart" said she.
He laughed, "It's yours if you want it
But you'll have to marry me".
The two have been together
And seen forty years depart,
Their love as true and lasting
As the small white pebble heart.

A Promise Kept

Anne collected stories in the way other people gather together teaspoons or postcards. Well why shouldn't she? It was after all her stock in trade. Each one was stored safely away in the safe box of her memory. Most of them lay there waiting quietly to be taken out when necessary. Okay, occasionally a few managed to escape.

There was a time when she scribbled down the things she heard or cut out from the papers reports that affected her in one way or another. This worked until there were so many scraps of paper she could never find the one she wanted, or else she got waylaid reading something and ended up wasting so much time searching that her brain lost its train of thought.

Some of the tales she was told made her laugh, some were silly, others were the happy-ever-after ones. Sometimes they were heart-breaking and she wanted to weep. Other times the things related filled her with horror or even anger and she would dwell on the different emotions for hours, until she realised she could not carry the weight of the world's sorrows on her slender shoulders.

Smiling a little sadly, she thought on the conversation she had had that morning with Valerie, the daughter of someone she had shared many bus journeys with, on their way to work, when they were teenagers.

Fay's family owned a local shop in their home town and were a respected and well liked family. When she was seventeen she fell completely and absolutely in love with Danny. They had known each other from childhood, even attending the same school.

Fay was often helping out in the shop when he came in. Nothing strange in that, until one fateful day when he forgot his wallet. As he fumbled about in his pockets, red faced with embarrassment, Fay told him not to worry. He could leave the money in the next time he was passing. Somehow it was as though they were seeing each other for the first time. From that day on they only had eyes for one another.

After a happy courtship, life followed its usual pattern. In due time they were married in a traditional way, with family and friends gathered round to help celebrate the occasion.

The lingering effects of the Second World War were still affecting the country. Few houses were available so they did what many young couples did at that time, and moved in with Fay's family. They were happy there and even after the birth of their only child, a little daughter, this was their home. When Fay's parents died the house became theirs and they lived a quiet, contented life for many years.

Sadly, a few years after their daughter married, a cruel blow was struck. Fay became ill. For a long time she lived a reasonably normal life until she had to spend week days in hospital, only coming home at the weekends.

Strangely, though she was well known and liked, no-one ever asked what was wrong. Country folk like to keep personal things close, and although everyone inquired after her, they sent their best wishes and left it at

that. The family's wish for silence about her illness was respected. Things didn't get any better. Eventually the whole week was spent in care, but still with the occasional drive or day out to celebrate birthdays and special occasions.

Later, sitting in her own kitchen, Anne recalled that morning's conversation. She had asked Valerie how her mother was doing.

"Ah", came the answer, "She's not doing well at all". Valerie shook her head, biting her lip to keep the tears at bay.

Unsure how to answer, Anne said, "I'm so sorry to hear that. When I think of your Mum I remember her beautiful clear blue eyes and infectious laugh. She was a joy to be with."

With a small nod, Valerie said, "She still has eyes as clear as ever and on good days the same great sense of humour. They told us at the start that anyone like Mum could live for eight years. We've been lucky. Mum has been with us for fourteen years. Dad sits with her for at least two hours every day. Sometimes she wants to talk and sometimes she doesn't. I go as often as I can but it's hard to watch the change. There are days when I can't face it and then I feel guilty." Anne sighed, "I'm sure it is. I've sat with loved ones and it is heart breaking. You all must be exhausted"

"We are", Valerie replied and then she gave the trace of a smile. We went to sit with her the other day, not knowing if she would want to talk or not, but when we sat down she was excited and said to Dad, "It's our anniversary today."

"I know", Dad told her. "We've been married for forty six years today" and he gave her a card and a piece of jewellery. Holding back tears, Valerie said, "Mum looked into Dad's eyes, put her hand on his knee and turning to me said, *I love him so much.* Isn't that wonderful. After forty-six years and all they have been through."

Anne herself was close to tears. She said, "That's so lovely. No matter what happens, you have that special memory to carry with you." She gave Valerie a hug and said, "When you see your Mum again, tell her I was asking for her and that I often think of the journeys we shared. We had some great times and many laughs. If she feels up to it she might tell you about some of our escapades."

The two parted. Anne with the mixed emotions of sadness for her friend's illness but with joy in the knowledge of the love Fay had shared all her life.

The word 'love' is often banded about with little thought, but there among the aisles of food in a supermarket, it had been lifted to its proper place and she had witnessed the words 'In sickness and in health' becoming a beautiful fact.

Remembering Love

My love, do you recall the lovely day
When first by happy chance we came this way?
Drawn on by country rose encrusted hedge,
And scented wild flowers peeping from the sedge.
Down the verdant lane the old mill stood
O'er grown with ivy and in sombre mood.
Without a care the birds sang all around,
The ancient water wheel made not a sound.

An elderly couple passed by hand in glove,
Each held the other's glance with eyes of love.
While we, with hearts entwined by silken bands
Of joy and trembling hope, our future planned.
We thought, this could be us one future day

When years roll on from youthful May.
With family grown and again with just we two,
We will return and seek this secret view.

Alas my love, I leave with a tender care
These precious ashes on a rock, from where
I sadly watch, with eyes half blind with tears,
My darling and my love, of wondrous years,
Be carried on his way by sluggish stream.
Our glad life now seems but a dream,
A weft and weave, worked by the hands of time,
We cannot fight but must to fate resign.

And so,
I leave you now my love, my shattered heart
An old abandoned nest,
With only memories to fill the never ending ache
Within my empty breast.

Making Plans

Hetty McAdoo was from a farming family. We knew each
other by sight as we were both in the local historical
society. Each year the society hired a bus and Archie
organised a day out, visiting places of interest to anyone
who was fond of ancient history. There was a lot of
walking on these days out. Comfortable shoes were a
must as quite an amount of time was spend clambering

over bramble covered dykes, stiles and gates, or carefully picking our way through long and often wet grass or muddy fields.

No matter who started out with whom, as the day went on we drifted along with ever changing companions. Hetty and I seemed to come together often that day. She was wonderful company and although close to eighty years of age at the time was hard to keep up with. She was one of those folk who were so full of life that they put the rest of us to shame.

Hetty loved travelling. She had been to places all over the world and related to me fascinating stories of walking on the Great Wall of China. She had visited Tiananmen Square a few weeks before the trouble erupted there. Kiev was another of her destinations. A beautiful place she remembered with pleasure. Strangely enough , once again she was there only a week or two before the explosion at the nuclear plant caused so much suffering and destruction.

"Do me a favour, Hetty". I said. "let me know where and when you are going on holiday and I'll make sure I go before you do. That way I might escape any trouble"

By this time we had reached the top of the mound and the eons old burial chamber with the huge stones marking the tomb of the honoured dead. Standing on the mound, with its mature trees and wonderful views of the surrounding countryside, we remarked how these ancient people always seemed to choose the most beautiful sites. Hetty turned and looked at me, as though trying to gauge my reaction to what she was about to say. "You'll never guess what I have been doing lately"

I laughed, "I haven't a clue but knowing you it could be anything. So what have you been doing?"

She smiled, "I've been looking around lots of graveyards."

"Why on earth would you want to do that?" I enquired.

"Well" she said, "I don't want to be buried somewhere I don't like. I want somewhere with a lovely view."

Again I laughed, "You are joking"

"No I'm not", she replied. "I want to like where I'm going to lie."

"But sure you'll know nothing about it. You'll not be looking at the view" I said.

"Oh I know that" was the reply. "but it's nice to know

where I'll be put, and it's pleasing to think that anybody, friend or stranger, who comes there will look around and say, isn't this a peaceful place. I'm not being morbid or anything. I'm really enjoying the search. I've seen some wonderful places, and let's be honest, we're all going to die sometime."

When the day was over we seldom saw one another as life took us in different directions. I never did find out if she found the place she could set her heart on. She had made plans for herself all her life, so why should her final resting place be left to other people to choose?

As the years go by there seems to be an awful lot of sense in what she was doing. To use Hetty's own words, "I'm not being morbid or anything". It just seems like a good idea.

I do hope she found the beautiful, peaceful spot she was searching for.

Nature's Magic

Some memories are imprinted on our minds forever. Not always earth shattering or life changing incidents, simply something that fills us with wonder, especially if seen through the eyes of a child.

Late one summer night, when I was small, my granda woke me from sleep saying there was something I had to see. He gave me my warm coat and when I was wrapped up and had shoes on my feet, we went outside to the piece of rough, open ground behind the row of houses we lived in, on the Ballyeaston Road. A few others were already there, all looking up at the sky.

"Look Janette. Look at that", said granda, wonder in his voice. "That's the Aurora Borealis."

Looking up there was a magical movement of many colours, greens, lemons, lilacs and blues, intermingling, dancing and waving across the sky. Granda took my hand and there we stood with the other people, on the rough ground with the open dunkills and dry lavatories on one side, on another the back of a butcher's shop, where pigs were reared and slaughtered. Back yards and a high, rusty tin roofed shed on the others and the remains of a bomb shelter beneath our feet. All forgotten as we saw nothing but the mystery and beauty above our heads, entranced by this seldom seen, at least in this part of the world, gift of nature. I for one will never forget that night, when we stood with upturned faces watching the magic in the sky.

These lines are my feeble attempt to put that memory into verse.

Aurora Borealis

Watching swirls of colour floating like ethereal light
I held my grandfather's hand, transfixed
And gazed in wonder at the sight.

While shades of green and lemon, blue and violet
Entwined in ever changing, silent dance.
A magic too heavenly to forget.

Despite the clods of earth beneath our feet,
The mundane, everyday around about,
Our spirits soared on high where angels meet.

The Germans are Coming

During the Second World War folks didn't travel far. Luckily in the North of Ireland you are never far from forest, lake or seaside. Larne was a favourite destination of my aunts Rhena, Madge and Sadie.

They would take the bus to the station and then enjoy the long walk to the shore, stopping at the little bakery close by to read the names of people who were slow to pay their bill, stuck up in the window. Sometimes they would buy a bun or two, always making sure to pay, of course. They never knew any of the people mentioned but they enjoyed the sense of outrage they shared that such a thing should be allowed to happen.

Then it was on to the Main Street, where they enjoyed the window displays in the various shops before heading for the shore at the Chaine Memorial.

Usually they would stop here and have the small picnic they had brought with them. Once the pangs of hunger had been satisfied they would dander along the sea front, stopping at the diving boards to watch the bathers – never once stripping off themselves. None of them could swim and to be seen paddling, without having the excuse of a child, would have been embarrassing.

One lovely summer day they were enjoying their afternoon out when a ship appeared out at sea and a few loud explosions sounded. Madge, always on the excitable side, screamed, "Oh my God it's the Germans. They're firing at us." And in spite of being on the fatter side of

plump she took off like a bat out of hell, up the steep slope of the Bank Heads, leaving the others trailing behind her. Never before had she been known to even break into a trot and apparently she never did so again for the rest of her life.

Later they discovered that it wasn't the Germans who had caused such panic. It was our own navy carrying out a training exercise.

Madge took the laughter caused by her mistake in good humour, which was just as well because she was never allowed to forget that particular day by the sea.

Goodbye to Childhood

A group of us were out for a meal. We were at the coffee and drink stage when the daughter of another friend walked in. "Oh my Lord", someone said. "Isn't it amazing how quickly children grow up".

Another chipped in, "I don't think I've ever grown up. If I see a puddle or a pile of leaves I want to splash and kick in them. I don't but I'd like to".

This started a conversation about when we felt we had left childhood behind. Many and varied were the stories. Not all painted a pretty picture of an ideal time growing up.

Liz, who has three daughters in their thirties now, related this tale. When I was in my thirties my father, whom I loved dearly, was diagnosed with a terminal illness. My mother had leant on him all her life and fell to pieces, so I needed to be strong. Trying to look after three almost teenage girls, hold down a job and help my mother to nurse my father nearly killed me. If it hadn't been for Jim (here she touched her husband's hand) I don't think I would have survived the two years we cared for Dad. After the funeral however I sagged. It was only then I permitted myself the luxury of tears. After the pain of losing Dad eased, I realised I'd truly become an adult and there was no going back.

I was one of the lucky ones who had a happy time growing up but it took forty years for me to do it.

William was next to tell his story. Here it is:

"My father was English and when we were young the

family lived in Manchester. There were two children, both boys. I was the elder by three years. Life was good in the early years. We didn't have a lot to spare but all the rest of our friends were in the same boat.

"Then disaster hit. Father lost his job on the railway when lines were closed in the Beecham era. My father couldn't get another job. Feeling useless made his life a misery and he turned to drink. He lay around the house getting morose and bad tempered. Mum struck it out until she could take no more. She left England and came back to Ireland to be near her family. Granny looked after us and Mum went back to work full-time. This worked for a couple of years but Gran got ill and Mum had to work only part-time. Often I was left to look after David. I was eleven years old and David was barely eight.

"The sense of responsibility lay heavy on my shoulders. I felt I had to protect my little brother and take some worry out of my Mum's life. I left the freedom of childhood behind and became the man of the house. That's when I grew up."

Linda too had an undesirable, miserable time until she was old enough to leave home and start a life of her own. This is her story:

"Both my parents were only children. Each of them had lost both mother and father before I was born. I've always wondered what it must be like to have dotting grandparents. Everyone always thinks that as an only child I must have been spoilt stupid. That would have been wonderful but sadly both my parents were recovering alcoholics. While they stayed away from the booze life was tolerable but they bickered constantly. At least during this time there was food on the table and the home was reasonably clean. Sadly these interludes were few and short-lived. They turned more and more often to whatever drink their money would stretch to. Many lonely, hungry nights were spent in an unheated house that often smelled of vomit. I tried to clean it up but never really got it all. I never asked anyone to the house. I never called it home. It was always just a house. I used to wash my school uniform every weekend. I was only eleven years old and ironing was a bit beyond me, so while all the other children looked neat and smart I was like a little gypsy child. The next five or six years were spent washing, cleaning, scrounging for food and trying to keep the peace. When I finished school I got a job and found a friend at work. We shared a flat until I got married. I don't remember growing up because I never had a childhood."

John gave a self-effacing laugh: "I had a wonderful time growing up. My parents weren't loaded but they lived simply. Money wasn't spent on style or fashion. Our home was comfortable and always full of life. There were six of us children, two boys and four girls. We shared our rambling old house with my mother's parents so we always had at least one grandparent to turn to, which was lovely. As a child I don't remember ever going on holiday, but that didn't matter. We grew up in the country so we wandered far and wide. There wasn't much cash to toss around but that didn't matter either. We took the dogs for walks through the fields, spent the odd day at the shore, enjoyed picnics in the hills or beside the river. Days were filled without planning. Activities just happened.

"Nights were seldom quiet. Sometimes neighbours dropped in for a chat. Other times the fiddlers came round. As well as fiddles there were banjos, accordions, bodhrans, mouth organs and flutes. Our place was where everyone congregated. Always it seemed there was laughter, joy and song. When someone got married the families often got together to have great nights and always there was a mixture of ages.

"When father died he had left a note telling us what music he wanted played at his wake and telling us to dance and have a toast to his long and happy life. There was sorrow and tears were shed of course, but we did as he asked and it was a send-off he would have been proud of.

"Mother was hale and hearty all her life and died as she would have wanted, suddenly and unexpectedly in her sleep. I made a bit of an ass of myself after her funeral. Not, thank the Lord, in public but in bed that night when the light was switched off. I remember feeling lost and a bit forlorn and turning to my wife, with tears streaming down my face, saying pathetically, 'I'm an orphan now'. I was fifty-six at the time. That was when I grew up."

Jan had a different experience: "I had a happy time as a child but when I was nine years old I came across something that confused me. The first time I saw the photograph I was searching for something in a chest of drawers. The chest sat in the bedroom I shared with my mother, aunt and grandmother. It was the large front upstairs room in a row of houses. There were two windows looking out to the road. Along with the chest of drawers there were two double beds sitting on the lino covered floor. At the side of each bed was a floral rug.

"A wardrobe, a three mirrored dressing table and a cane chair with gold tipped edges furnished the room. The photograph lay face down on the bottom of the bottom drawer. Folded away with it was a shiny sheet of coloured paper with some print on it. Filled with the curiosity of childhood, I turned the photo over to find myself looking at a sepia tinted wedding party. There were six people, two men and four ladies looking back at me. Two of the ladies were seated on upright chairs in the

studio study so popular at that time. I recognised two of the bridesmaids as my aunts. The other was a stranger as were the two men. The bride was my mother.

"Minutes passed as I stared at the faces, trying in vain, with my young innocent brain, to make some order out of the scene. In the back of my mind some instinct told me that the man standing beside my mother must be my father. I studied the face, looking for something I could recognise, waiting for some forgotten memory. No emotion of any sort presented itself. Looking back I realise this was the day I left childhood behind me. Something stopped me from asking any questions.

"The sepia image with its black suited men and ladies in long slipper satin gowns, almost hidden behind huge sprays of roses, carnations, ivy, fern and ribbons, head dresses and veils framing the faces with their fixed smiles, frozen in time, this along with its slip of paper containing a baby's name, were replaced, upside down, exactly as they had been, on the bottom of the drawer. I never saw the men again. No, I think that may not be true. Three years later, when I was twelve years old, my paternal grandmother, whom I'd never met, died. For some inexplicable reason I was put on a bus and sent to attend her funeral. Walking up to the house and knocking on the door of people I had never met, entering into a room full of family members I had never known and who didn't know me, was one of the worst experiences of my life. I knew I was being talked about and that they'd rather I wasn't there. Eventually it was time to go home. A man who hadn't spoken to me all day walked me down the short lane to the bus stop. As the bus approached he reached me a florin then turned and walked away.

"Back home, as soon as it was possible, when no-one would see me, I sneaked upstairs and brought out the hidden photograph and the sheet of paper. I searched the face for recognition but the man standing beside my mother woke no sort of response, dark hair seemed to be the only link. So who was the man who walked me down the lane? Was he a family friend, an uncle or was he my father? I'll never know. What I do know is, if it was him, all he ever gave me, apart from my name, was a silver two shilling piece. No, again this is not true. He gave me life, the most important thing of all. The owner of the name on the christening roll of a church is still a mystery. All I do know is that the baby boy had the same parents as I did."

After we had all told our stories we spoke about how our young lives had affected us. We all agreed that our parents, good or bad, had coped as best they could and none of us had any right to judge or blame them because once we reach adulthood or at least be able to provide for ourselves, we have only ourselves to thank or blame for the people we become.

Last Chance

With vague apologies to those who like to take offence.
I have often thought that whatever powers there be must throw up their hands in horror at the mess we humans are making of life here on Earth. Sometimes I imagine what would happen if they got fed up with us.

The eternal spirits were answering a call of The Great One to discuss a troublesome little planet called Earth. Earth had, as an experiment, been left to its own devices for untold eons but was now causing trouble. One group, using the cover name 'Mankind' had accumulated enough knowledge to gain the upper hand over all other creatures on the planet.

The Great One spoke feelingly to impress on those gathered together that something needed to be done. The most senior and most dependable of the spirits was the one most despised by the Earthlings because of the choices offered. Satan was the tempter of Mankind, wandering unseen among the people, listening and reporting back to the spirits at each new gathering.

Occasionally, in an attempt to guide them, the

WAR GREED POWER STARVATION NEED HATE

alternatives of war or peace, help or hindrance, kindness or cruelty, were given. Sadly, more often than not, the wrong one was chosen. Greed, ambition and a desire for power had become the driving force. When asked to explain, Satan's reply began with a shake of the head." I fear we must intervene. Few are content with the circumstances they find themselves in. There are disagreements among nations and people. Once they shared and helped one another but the importance of 'I' 'Me' and 'Mine' seems to have smothered every kind or helpful thought.

To keep prices high food is destroyed while millions starve. Those in need, the poor, those not perfect in body, the young and the very old, are often treated worse than the dogs in the street. There are various religions. The followers of each religion or sect claim that they alone know how everyone should live. Those in charge are often corrupted by their power and a desire to wipe out anyone with differing ideas There is a dangerous, angry, edgy acceptance by the masses that could erupt at any time.

The most worrying thing is that the Earthlings are now talking of expanding out to the rest of the Galaxy. They must never be allowed to spread their contamination".

The Guardians agreed. Satan was given more powers to test Mankind. They were to be given one more chance before the final decision on annihilation would be taken.

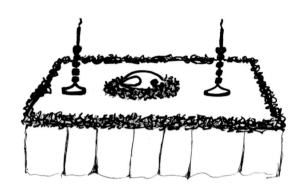

A Christmas Wish
(Sometimes life takes its toll)

I've got a wish for Christmas,
Now the children are grown up,
With little families of their own,
And oh, I wish them luck

With all the love and sorrow,
Disappointments and successes.
The angry words, the cruel jibs,
The kisses, the caresses.

The joy of happy laughter,
The sparkling children's eyes
When they open Santa's presents
And parents act surprised.

Now there's just the two of us,
We look across the table
At the stranger sitting opposite
With wife or husband label.

He's fond of me, and I of him,
But life pushed us apart.
While he had work and mates and sport
The children took my heart.

Oh how I wish we could recall,
When days were far too short
For all the things we had to share,
And a love so deep it hurt.

But here we sad and lonely sit
With festive fare this Christmas Day
Two sad and lonely people
Searching for something to say.

The Unspeakable Word

We all know that life has to end in death, yet it is an
unspeakable word. We are afraid of even the sound of it.
No one wants to face up to the fact, yet we have to when
it comes to our own front door.

Few people escape having to live with the sadness of
nursing someone we love through failing health. Most of
us have sat there in helpless silence beside the one whose
life is slowly fading away, or we try to speak of light
hearted things, though this is usually a one sided
conversation; the person in the bed has already, in one
part of their mind, stepped away from us. Still there we
sit forcing a smile, terrified of letting our misery show for
fear of upsetting our loved one. Tears are always present

behind our set smiles and one slip of our emotions would open the flood gates of sorrow.

So there we sit trying to lift the spirits of the dying. Speaking of things the children are doing or of some silly story we've heard, when in our minds there are a million questions we would like to ask or words of love and thanks we would like to say. There are the words that would tell them how much they will be missed and how much they mean to us. We never say them. Instead, you are, like me, trapped in the stoic nature, common to those of us born in this part of Ireland.

"You have to stay strong". I hear the mantra ringing in my ears. The words seem to be engraved on my very soul. When at last the loved one is at peace, did you, like me, question yourself? Should I have poured out my grief to the dying, or would that have been, as I felt at the time, a selfish indulgence?

Was it right to hide my feelings in a cloak of silence? We wonder and turn the question over and over in our minds feeling a little guilty. Maybe this or that word should have been spoken. Our sense of loss leads us to ask, "Did I do the right thing?"

Perhaps no matter what we did or will do, it is a question we will always ask. Sadly it is one we will never get the answer to.

Individual Christmas

Listening to the radio or watching television we're given the impression that each person in every family should celebrate Christmas in the same way. This makes a lot of folk think they are missing out on something that is almost a birthright.

The build up to Christmas raises expectations of this marvellous day when whole families share a wonderful experience. Children are encouraged by ads on television to ask for ever more expensive gifts. Parents are afraid to say no because other parents will be giving them and no one wants their child to be the odd one out.

When this wonderful experience doesn't happen, and it seldom does, they begin to feel that they have been cheated in some way. Before the population was led astray by the glittering and sickenly sweet Hollywood fable, in each household Christmas was celebrated within their means and without the need to pile up massive debts to keep up with the things we are now told are necessary for a successful day, folk did their own thing.

My Christmases were spent among a family of adults, two aunts, an uncle, my granda and my mother. When I was school age there were the usual Santa surprises, a stocking in bed and then downstairs a box of sweets, usually Quality Street, books, Girls' Crystal, The Eagle (I loved Dan Dare) and Girl Annuals, some clothes and the big present. One year it was a Timex watch. Another year, to my amazement and disbelief, I got a bicycle. HEAVEN!

Once I started work the format changed. Everyone bought everyone else one gift so we each had five things to buy and five things to receive. When Christmas morning arrived we all came downstairs and had a breakfast of bacon, egg, soda and fadge, before going back upstairs to bring down the presents. There we'd sit, goodies on our knees, "Who's going first?" someone would ask. It was of course always Granda. His gifts were handed round. Only one person opened at a time giving us a chance to admire what had been given. And so it continued until everyone had handed over and opened their presents.

Shortly after this Mum and I would head across to see Aunt Maggie, Uncle Alex and their daughter Margaret, who lived in Mulholland Terrace on the Doagh Road, to wish them a Happy Christmas. Then it was a longer dander to Hollybush Gardens in Millvale to see their son Jim and his wife Nessie and their children Jim and Laura, to see what Santa had delivered.

When we said cheerio to them it was on to the prefabs to call on Mum's sister Sadie and her husband Maurice

Weston, who was often known as 'Angy' (apparently this was what men from his part of England were known by as a nickname) and their children, twins Norma and Jean and their son Harry. This was always a longer visit where a cup of tea and a slice of home baked Christmas cake was enjoyed to sustain us on the walk back to the Ballyeaston Road.

To make life a bit easier and so that no-one had to work hard on the holiday we never had Christmas dinner. Instead at lunch time we had a bowl of lovely thick chicken broth and a couple of boiled potatoes and Christmas pudding with custard for afters. In the evening a salad was served with succulent roast chicken. Granda was a postman and one of the farmers on his round always supplied a large plump fowl. Afterwards we had a wonderful spread of all sorts of home made buns.

All in all a happy, quiet relaxed day as most of the food was prepared before the 25th. When Granda brought the fowl home it had to be plucked and cleaned. He and I would close the scullery door and set to work preparing the chicken for cooking.

Boxing Day was when all the family congregated at number 37. Usually it was a crowd of about fourteen but it was an open door and all friends were welcome to drop in for a yarn and a bite to eat. The food was a repeat of the previous day's evening meal.

All the downstairs rooms were needed. The front room, or parlour, was usually reserved for wakes, wedding parties, courting and of course entertaining, the middle room, known then as the kitchen, was where we lived and ate everyday and the scullery where cooking, washing, ironing and bathing were done. At this time we had an outside lavatory at the bottom of the back yard. The running water, only cold, was just being put into our home, so there was as yet no inside bathroom.

The drop leaf table was opened to its full extent, a beautiful hand embroidered table cloth was spread and the table set. There was no central heating so the fires were lit. Those with their chairs close to the fire sometimes had to squeeze past other diners to go out to the yard to cool down. We'd fill the day with songs, stories, rhymes, stupid jokes and silly games before the visitors trooped home full of happy memories.

The first time I had a full Christmas dinner was at my mother-in-law's home. This too was wonderful though most ate too much a fell asleep in their chairs afterwards. Mrs McKendry was a good cook and it's her I have to blame or thank for introducing me to the joy of a steaming 'hot whiskey'.

Each family builds up its own customs. When I married we followed the Christmas dinner idea but with cold meat and salad at night, followed of course by a variety of buns and tray bakes and we always followed the open door idea of my own family.

It's nice to do your own thing. Forget the hype. Don't follow the crowd. Just enjoy yourself.

When It's Your Own Fault

When was the last time you did something stupid? Something, that when you've done it, you can't quite believe that you didn't learn anything from the last time it happened, or even the time before that.

When I joined Marie, Anita and Frank the three of them were in deep discussion.

"Sure I can't believe it happened. You would have thought I'd know better by now." Anita said in her lilting Donegal accent.

Marie joined in the moan, "I know. I do it too and every time I tell myself I'll remember not to, but it makes no difference. I still do it."

When I appeared they explained the different reasons behind their complaining.

Anita had left the hot water tap running, forgetting that

the water got hotter the longer it ran. Then without thinking she put her hand underneath the offending tap to wash a cup. Scream, yelps and pain in that order. Then the annoyance of knowing that she'd done the same thing time and time again.

"Do we never learn?" she asked.

Marie's complaint was different. For a third time in two weeks she'd locked herself out of her house. She shook her head. "I keep meaning to get another key cut and leave it where I can find it, or with a neighbour. I go down the street with good intentions but come back home and realise I've still done nothing about a key."

Frank stood up and limped over to pour a cup of tea. "What's wrong with you?" we wanted to know.

"Don't ask", was the gruff reply before he proceeded to tell us. "You know how I like gardening. Well last night when it was almost dark I went for a walk round the back garden in my slippers and stepped on an upturned rake I'd left lying on the grass."

Though we felt sorry for him we each gave a snort of disbelief. Frank is usually so precise about what he's doing we never imagined he'd leave anything lying around, especially on his treasured lawn.

"I know", he said, "I'd laugh too if it wasn't so sore and I wasn't so angry with myself. You might not believe me but this isn't the first time I've done the same thing."

"What about you?" they asked me. I held out a hand with a few white scars and a fresh blister.

"What happened? How did you manage that?"

Shame faced I owned up. "It was the grill. Instead of using the handle provided or an oven glove like you're supposed to, I used my bare hand."

It's a good job I wasn't looking for sympathy for none was forthcoming. "Stupid edjit" was the mildest comment.

We all agreed that we should learn from our mistakes but, you know the old adage 'Familiarity breeds contempt'. Perhaps we are conditioned by some fault in our genes, to make the same mistakes over and over again. Or maybe it's just a case of downright laziness.

Saturday Night Out In Larne

Young folk now-a-days are wise to the ways of the world. Television and magazines along with radio and films mean that they are educated in things we were naive about or lived in ignorance of. Having a drink of alcohol was one area we knew little of. Apart from a bottle of port or sherry being brought in at Christmas or when there was a wedding in the house alcohol played no part in our lives so we had no need to know much about it.

Few people had cars so when one was available as many of us as possible piled in. There was no law on seat belts so manufacturers never put them in. One Saturday night when, joy of joys, a car was able to be borrowed, it was decided to go to the dance held in The King's Arms in Larne. The car was a little Morris Minor and into this small space we managed to squeeze four girls and four

boys. When the driver parked the car and we all piled out, a policeman nearby watched open-mouthed, shook his head in disbelief and walked away.

Being a bit early for the dance we went into McNeill's Hotel for a drink. The girls had never been for an alcoholic drink before so we were a bit nervous. I suppose we could have asked for a soft drink but that would have made us look too young. We were seventeen or eighteen at the time and wanted to look as if we knew what we were doing. It would never do to look young and untutored in the ways of the grown-up world.

The boys were probably feeling exactly the same. They too were putting up a front. Anyway in we went and plonked ourselves down on the beautifully upholstered seats. After a few moments a waiter appeared. Oh dear, what to order? The first girl asked for a gin and orange (it was the only drink she had heard of). The rest of us followed suit. So there we were, all sitting with a drink we'd never tasted before. The first sip was a shock to the system and not a pleasant one. We were all totally surprised to find that it was like drinking perfume. Still we managed to finish our glasses but refused point blank any offer of another drink.

Thank goodness it was now time for the music and dancing in The King's Arms. There was no disappointment here and everyone had a great time.

As we crammed ourselves back into the car we discovered that we had picked up another passenger. He'd missed his lift and had no way of getting home so somehow or other we managed to make room and everyone arrived home safe and sound. Great end to a great night, gin and orange excluded.

Acceptance

I thought I heard you call my name
And turned around to see.
I found it was a gentle breeze
Singing through a tree.

I thought I saw you smile at me,
And quickly hurried near
But found a rose lit by the sun,
Instead of you, my dear.

I thought I smelt you near me,
Joyous I turned and found
Instead of you, my darling
A primrose strewn ground.

Something soft caressed my cheek.
Touching in hope and fear,
I found only a raindrop
Merging with a tear.

I miss your scent, I miss your touch
And oh, to hear your song,
Or see you smile and taste your lips
But you, my love, are gone.

The Invitation

Wrapping her hands around a welcome cup of coffee Neave gave a sigh of satisfaction. Her spirits were high. She had just posted off a cheque, clearing her last debt. For the first time in fifteen years she was free from the fear of threatening calls and demanding letters.

As she looked out over the front garden the postman walked to her front door. The letter box rattled and there was a plop as something dropped to the floor. Neave lifted the firm cream envelope wondering what it could be. When she opened it a gold printed card invited her to a wedding. Her heart sank as she read it. The invitation was from people she liked but from whom she never expected a request to attend their wedding.

Pound signs began dancing before her eyes. The service was being held almost sixty miles away and the reception thirty miles further out. She'd have to hire a car for the day. (She had sold her old jalopy and couldn't afford another car at the moment). A day off work meant losing a day's pay. She had nothing suitable to wear so would need a new outfit. Then there was the cost of a few drinks at the bar and of course a wedding present. The whole day would cost at least four hundred pounds. This would take her back into debt. She really could not afford it. It wasn't as if they were family or even close friends. Yes, she enjoyed their company but four hundred pounds!

She did what she always did when difficult decisions had to be made. She procrastinated. Tomorrow she would decide what to do. The invitation with its R.S.V.P. was put behind the clock. Three weeks later, when she was out shopping, a voice behind her said, "Oh, I was hoping I would bump into you. We haven't had your reply yet so I am taking it for granted that you are coming or you would have let me know".

Mortified, Neave nodded, smiled brightly and replied, "Of course I'm coming. I wouldn't miss it for the world". When they parted she called herself all sorts of stupid idiot. Why she asked herself had she not ticked the *'Sorry I can't attend'* box as soon as the invitation had arrived and just sent a small gift. She was feeling depressed until an idea sprang to mind, putting a glimmer of hope on the horizon. She could get sick, very, very sick, two days before the event and opt out.

In the end she went to the wedding thanks to her credit card.

Education and the Thinking Man

Now-a-days the population has become steeped in the idea that the trouble has always been between Roman Catholics and Protestants. This is not strictly true. There was a third group – the original Presbyterians. Down the years this has been forgotten.

In 1798 there was a rebellion against the unfair laws and treatment meted out by the ruling Protestant Anglican ascendancy, This was led, in the South by the Catholic community and in the North it was the Presbyterians, who would never have referred to themselves as protestants, who took the lead.

The area round the Sixmile Valley was a hot bed of rebellion. The main reasons for 'The Turnout' as the rebellion was called, were that everyone, no matter what their faith, had to pay tithes to the established church and Presbyterian marriages in their own meeting houses were not recognised and children from such marriages were considered bastards.

The early Presbyterians refused to subscribe to The Westminster Confessions of Faith. Education was thought to be unnecessary for the common people but Presbyterians regarded it as a right. They believed that everyone should be able to read and understand the Bible for themselves, led by their conscience. Those who taught in the hedgerow schools were often arrested and thrown in jail.

Though the Rising failed changes came about because of it. The establishment tried to bribe Presbyterian

ministers to persuade their flock to accept the
Confessions of Faith by payment of money. Many did
and they became the largest group of Presbyterians.
Many didn't and still don't. The Non-subscribing
Presbyterian Church is one of these groups.

In the 1800s the treatment, brutality, cruelty and
savagery, that the Crown forces used against the rebels
was still very much alive in living memory.

One change was that all children were permitted to go
to school. Archibald McIlroy tells of one local school in
the late 1800s. The school building stood at the side of the
Square, opposite the Town Hall. A Mr Graham taught in
the upstairs room, which was reached by an outside
stone staircase on the upper side of the building. He was
fond of telling everyone how he had graduated from
Trinity College, Dublin with a very high degree. Locally
he was known as 'Fractions'.

Mr Graham cared about the boys, many of whom came to school barefoot and without food in their stomach. Fractions often had a large black iron pot of soup on the go. This was cooked over the open fire he kept alight as best he could, supplementing the meagre fuel allowance from his own pocket.

Once when the soup was ready and was being handed round an inspector arrived. This inspector was outraged. How dare the teacher be doing this. It would be reported to the authorities in Dublin. He ordered that no more soup be made and threatened dire consequences if he was not heeded. No attention was paid to his complaint. Fractions reckoned that as far as the boys were concerned, getting sustenance into them was a matter of greater urgency than what the men in Dublin thought.

One treat, beloved by all, was 'the black ball', a sort of gobstopper sweet, which was handed round. Each boy was allowed a suck before passing it on to the next eager mouth.

Ah, the joys of schooldays long ago.

Disillusioned

I used to think that life was fair and folk got their just desserts. Good was repaid with a bonus and evil cost more in retribution than was worth the effort. But it seems life is not like that.

I used to think that those in high places, such as government, church, policing, teaching and leaders of youth organisations and charity workers were above reproach. But it seems life is not like that.

I used to think that the words that came out of someone's mouth were truly meant and weren't just so much hot air. I used to think that all religions worked for the good of mankind. I used to think that any grown up would help a child. But life is not like that.

I used to think that love, romantic love, was the truest form of the word. I didn't realise that this sort of feeling is not lavished without cost, or that friendship is a greater and more important kind of love.

I used to think that my hopes for a better world would come true. But it seems life is not like that.

I don't want to leave you with this miserable thought so this wish is my leaving thought.

A Wish

I wish you health and happiness.
I wish you God's good grace.
May many of your dreams come true.
May one be left to chase.

When opportunity comes by
And knocks upon your door,
Welcome her with open arms
And dance across the floor.

May poverty and pain pass by
While love and laughter stay.
May pleasant dreams be yours at night
And joy in life by day.